D0510689

Getting the builders in

... and staying in control

Where to find _Right Way_

Elliot _Right Way_ take pride in our editorial quality, accuracy and value-for-money. Booksellers everywhere can rapidly obtain any _Right Way_ book for you. If you have been particularly pleased with any one title, do please mention this to your bookseller as personal recommendation helps us enormously.

Please send to the address on the back of the title page opposite, a stamped, self-addressed envelope if you would like a copy of our _free catalogue_. Alternatively, you may wish to browse through our extensive range of informative titles arranged by subject on the Internet at **www.right-way.co.uk**

We welcome views and suggestions from readers as well as from prospective authors; do please write to us or e-mail:
info@right-way.co.uk

Getting the Builders in

... and staying in control

by

Paul J Grimaldi

RIGHT WAY
plus

Copyright notice

© Elliot Right Way Books MMIII.

All rights reserved. No part of this book may be reproduced, stored in a retrieval system, or transmitted, in any form or by any means, electronic, photocopying, mechanical, recording or otherwise, without the prior permission of the copyright owner.

Conditions of sale
This book shall only be sold, lent, or hired for profit, trade, or otherwise, in its original binding, except where special permission has been granted by the Publisher.

Whilst care is taken in selecting Authors who are authoritative in their subjects, it is emphasised that their books can reflect their knowledge only up to the time of writing. Information can be superseded and printers' errors can creep in. This book is sold, therefore, on the condition that neither Publisher nor Author can be held legally responsible for the consequences of any error or omission there may be.

Typeset in 11pt Legacy Serif Book by Letterpart Ltd., Reigate, Surrey.

Printed and bound in Great Britain by Mackays of Chatham Ltd.

The *Right Way Plus* series is published by Elliot Right Way Books, Brighton Road, Lower Kingswood, Tadworth, Surrey, KT20 6TD, U.K. For information about our company and the other books we publish, visit our website at www.right-way.co.uk

About the author

Paul Grimaldi has worked in the construction industry for 30 years in the area of building services design and project management both in the commercial and domestic sectors. He has worked with architects, consultants, subcontractors and builders and spent six years as a partner in a small contracting firm. As contractor, consultant and home-owner, he has seen all sides of most construction situations.

Acknowledgements

The author is grateful to the following individuals and organisations for assistance with technical and background information:

Harri Hughes, Bob Abbott and Bill Flanagan, surveyor, solicitor and Building Control officer respectively, with whom I have had the pleasure of working and who have added their useful comments to my drafts.

Chris Halliday, an architect familiar with the trials and tribulations of working with contractors and private clients. Bruce Coey, a Planning officer. Mike Hodgeson, a structural engineer, whose expertise I know I can trust because the beam he designed for my kitchen is still supporting by bedroom.

Trading Standards officers, Nicola Tudor in Tower Hamlets and Gary Edel in Barnet – I hope I have done justice to their comments.

Colin Eeles and Christine Macklen for objective feedback and proof reading.

Thanks also to the various others who have contributed through allowing me to bounce off ideas or by sharing their experiences.

Finally, to Elliot Right Way Books for having the faith to run with the idea and apart from a few useful suggestions, letting me get on with the book pretty well unhindered.

Contents

List of illustrations

Introduction

Improving our homes gives us additional comfort, more space and a leg up the property ladder, without the hassle of moving house. Yet the fear of employing a 'cowboy builder' and the construction disaster stories featured on TV can lead to the view that moving might be simpler.

Nightmare builders may be the exception but delays in completion, mushrooming "unforeseen" costs, and disputes about workmanship are all too common when homeowners employ contractors.

Even though the odds of finding a complete rogue are relatively small, there is a 'lottery' element to flicking through classified ads. Many competent contractors can be under resourced and unhelpful when complications arise. And who is to blame when the final job is not as you envisaged or is twice the price? A large number of reported disputes about domestic construction work are a result of poor communication or misunderstandings about what was agreed when the contractor gave his quotation. Others are a result of the client's lack of experience or knowledge of construction protocols.

With this book I have tried to unravel the intricacies of household repair, renovation and extension projects and to provide you with the resources to manage the work from conception to completion. I cannot guarantee that after reading this book you will only employ 'good' contractors, although I hope it will help you to avoid some of the worst. More realistically, you should gain the knowledge and confidence to ask the right questions, to stay in control and take appropriate action if you feel that things are going wrong.

The book explains what issues you need to consider before you engage a contractor, how to communicate what you want, how to control costs, how to deal with 'extras' and what to do if you become dissatisfied. It is not a complete practical guide to domestic construction works, although it includes guidance to help you to produce a detailed brief and subsequently converse with (and keep an eye on) the contractor. For a more detailed technical understanding of construction works, there are technical books available. If detailed knowledge is needed for design purposes you should hire a professional; construction design is not a safe DIY activity. I have included advice on finding and engaging architects, engineers and draughtsmen.

The guidance given is appropriate for most domestic work and it may be useful for some commercial work of a similar scale. Of course all self-help books have their limitations. If you intend to construct a complete new home or a new wing to your 18th century manor house, whilst this book may assist your understanding, you would be wise to employ an architect both to design and project manage the works.

For smaller jobs like decoration and repairs, you may need to make some judgment about how formally you deal with the contractor and scale down some of the suggestions so that they fit the work more appropriately. Chapter 1 deals specifically with some of the difficulties associated with minor repairs and emergencies.

In Chapter 2, I have described how major construction projects are managed and how that management can be applied to household renovation and improvement works.

In Chapter 3, I have outlined a variety of considerations that may be useful before you launch into discussing the work with contractors. The remaining chapters plot the course of a typical project and deal with the various stages and issues that you may need to address.

'Packaged' works such as double-glazing, central heating

etc., although being more of an adjusted off-the-peg suit than a bespoke tailor-made garment, can be quite complex so I have made particular note of these works where applicable.

The UK construction industry has an unfortunate reputation for being adversarial, and recent government reports have highlighted the loss of production and the cost of this tradition. Partnership and co-operation is the way forward. It is not my intention, therefore, to make you suspicious and untrusting of contractors. This book, at its most simple level, is to provide awareness and to help you differentiate between genuine contractors and outright crooks. When dealing with bona-fide contractors, mutual respect is what is required. A contractor needs to respect your desires, your quality standards and your budget. Equally you must respect the contractor's need for adequate and timely information and his need to cover his costs and make a reasonable profit. This will be the best route to a smooth running project. The relationship remains that of a business transaction, so information needs to be carefully exchanged and recorded to reduce the likelihood of ambiguity and disputes.

A word about gender. It is a quirk of our language that the third person pronouns and many occupational nouns are gender specific. Homeowners come in both genders although there are more men than women on most building sites. Where, for the sake of easy reading I have used the words he or his, please take this also to mean she or her and take occupations ending in ' ..man' to be short for 'hu-man'.

The advice offered in this book is as accurate as reasonably possible at the time of writing. Regulations, materials and other information will change over time and guidance on legal issues is general. Any technical matters or points of law must be verified in the context of readers' own situations.

Chapter 1:

"Small Works"*

Urgent repair work

Dealing with small, urgent repairs is a different matter from keeping tabs on a whole project. There is little opportunity to 'manage' the process and it is a field in which many of the industry's more dubious characters like to operate. There are a number of perils to avoid:

- Calling out the wrong type of tradesman.
- Poor quality repairs.
- Contractor carrying out unnecessary work.
- Over charging.

If the cause of the problem is not obvious, try to do a little careful investigation of your own. But don't do anything that could risk unnecessary further damage or, more importantly, your own safety.

For instance, if water pours through the ceiling, identify the source. In this case, there are generally two likely causes: a broken water pipe or a hole in the roof. The former will require a plumber and the latter a roofing contractor. There is also a difference between a plumber and a heating engineer. Identifying the appropriate trade will avoid abortive call-out charges.

---

* Several medium and larger construction firms have a "small works" section that carries out repairs and smaller projects. The definition is variable but I have borrowed it to cover smaller household jobs like emergency and general repairs.

Selecting contractors is covered in Chapter 8. In an emergency there may be little time for careful selection but there may be time to ask neighbours if they can either recommend someone or advise whom to avoid! If using Yellow Pages or local press, choose a nearby firm with membership of a suitable trade or professional organisation (details in Chapter 7). Your second call should be to that association to verify that the contractor is a current member (see Appendix 7). If you have the time, i.e. if it is not a real emergency, compare call out charges, hourly rates and 'percentage profit' on materials over the telephone.

With some urgent work, the cause of the problem is unclear, e.g. a blocked drain, no heating, a blown fuse, etc. and you will be reliant upon the contractor to investigate. This is a danger area because it provides the crook in overalls with ample opportunity to sell unnecessary work. Typical examples are: digging up several metres of drainage when 5 minutes with an unblocking tool would suffice; replacing a boiler when a £5 part would solve the problem. Following the guidelines below will minimize your chances of being ripped off here.

WHEN THE CONTRACTOR ARRIVES

i) Note the time: if you are being charged on an hourly rate basis – time is money!

ii) If the cause of the problem is not obvious, tell the contractor to let you know as soon as he has discovered what has happened. If you don't hear from him after 15 minutes, check what he is doing. Don't be blinded with science. Any practical work can be explained, broadly, in lay terms and usually demonstrated.

iii) Ask what options you have – e.g. repair or replacement. Take notes. Ask how long each option will take, how much it will cost and whether it can be done immediately. If the price is over about £50 ask for it to be broken down into labour and materials. (Average

iv)   labour rate in 2002 is £120-£160 per day. Material prices can be checked with a builders' merchant.)

iv)   Decide if you want the contractor to proceed with a full repair or temporary repair so that you can obtain other prices. You are not obliged to accept the contractor's price or diagnosis! See below.

v)   Keep an eye on work carried out, check the time when he finishes and ensure you obtain a written detailed bill. Obtain a receipt for any cash payment. Cheque payments are preferable, credit cards are even better; they provide additional protection through the issuing company.

"Oooo I'm afraid you've got a problem 'ere"

Make an effort to understand the problem, and if you write down everything that the contractor says, he will be less inclined to give false information. If you give the message "It's all too technical for me" a rogue contractor will hear "I'm a mug, please take me for a ride"!

Call out charges and hourly rates are appropriate for emergency work because at the time of your call the contractor (or the 'call centre') does not know what problem may be found. Yet an hourly rate provides no incentive for the contractor to get the job done quickly – in fact it provides an opportunity for the dishonest contractor to drag out the job for as long as he thinks he can – especially if business is a bit slow. If you are told that more extensive work is required – more than about £100 worth, obtain alternative fixed sum prices based on the emergency contractor's assessment of what needs to be done. Explain to other contractors that you want a free quotation.

Heating

Heating engineers are obliged by law to disconnect unsafe gas appliances, although this should only happen if the appliance cannot be made safe in any other way without a return visit. If you are told that an appliance is obsolete and needs to be replaced, contact the manufacturers (whose name will be on the appliance somewhere) and verify that parts can no longer be obtained. Obtain competitive prices for replacing the appliance.

Roofing

If a roofing contractor, called out because of a single drip in the loft, insists that a complete new roof is required, ask him if he can effect a temporary repair. With the initial problem dealt with, you can consider, in your own time, whether or not further work is required and obtain competitive prices.

Drainage

If a drainage contractor, called out to deal with a blockage, insists that a drain has collapsed, always get a second opinion. Collapses do happen but not as often as they are 'repaired'. Most blockages can be jetted through or broken up in minutes with special tools. Some firms will use Closed Circuit TV cameras to illustrate their point. However, whilst useful, CCTV pictures take a lot of careful analysis because their wide angle lenses exaggerate cracks and ridges which are not really serious. If there is a collapse that requires excavation, this will show up on the CCTV screen as broken pipe, probably with soil or gravel in the drain. If you are convinced that excavation is necessary, be present when the drain is *carefully* uncovered to witness the discovery of the obstruction or collapse.

Electrical

If your problem is electrical, some re-wiring may be suggested because an electrician should not simply make a repair to an unsafe circuit. Ask why a re-wire is necessary. If the cables are coated with rubber, fabric or lead, the wiring is probably quite old. PVC has been used since the 1970s. If the insulation is falling off the wires or is brittle and cracking, it needs replacing. If the old wiring appears indistinguishable from new cables, you have every right to be suspicious. If you are unconvinced, ask the contractor to make the circuit safe – which may mean removing the fuse – and obtain a second opinion. If you have an old cast iron fuse box on a timber board it should be replaced. If you have a box with plastic fronted fuse holders these can be replaced with circuit breakers, but this is not essential.

CHARGES

Charges should equate with the hourly rate quoted and any material costs should be clearly detailed. If you believe that you are being overcharged, pay what you think is fair based on the price you were quoted, the time taken and the cost of any materials used. (If you did not ask for a price, you have no basis on which to argue.) You can check the price of the materials later, with an appropriate merchant. (A small percentage profit on materials is appropriate although contractors will obtain discounts on retail prices.) If you have refused to pay the full invoice value, write to the company explaining why. If you are acting reasonably, you will probably hear no more. Do not be intimidated by the contractor.

You may encounter one little ruse where charges are based on so much per hour "or part thereof": if the job has taken just 55 minutes, your caller may take an extra 10 minutes to sit in his van and write out the bill or rearrange his toolbox, just to push him into the next hour. Some plumbers have been known to sit in the loft for 10 minutes occasionally tapping the side of the water tank while the minutes tick into the next hour. If you suspect this type of nonsense, advise your tradesman that you pay only for the time taken to carry out the work and a reasonable amount of time for paperwork – nothing for spinning out the time.

I have concentrated here on plumbing, heating and electrical work because apart from locksmiths and glaziers whose work is easily seen, these are the trades most commonly required to deal with emergencies. Most work to building fabric with the exception of holes in the roof, even if rather urgent, is rarely a matter of emergency.

Routine repairs and replacements

Chapter 6 explains about contracts and briefs for larger projects. While detailed formal documentation may be excessive for smaller repair work (as detailed here), the essential elements of that chapter should be noted and adapted to suit smaller works. Below are the basic steps you should take for routine repairs and replacements.

- Identify the full scope of the work required. You may need to discuss the details with contractors before you are sure what is needed.
- Obtain three or four firm competitive prices (two or three for very small jobs). Ensure that all contractors are pricing for the same thing and that they include options if necessary (see Chapter 8).
- Obtain references (see Chapter 8).
- Consider matters of access, cleanliness and safety.
- Agree payment terms – avoid deposits (see Chapter 8).
- Agree start time and period for the work.
- Confirm all agreements in a letter to the selected contractor.

Some firms specialising in emergency work may suggest charging a call-out fee just to offer a price. If the job is straightforward and you know exactly what is required, use only firms who are willing to provide a free quotation.

If a contractor provides a quotation with little detail of what work he has allowed for, yet his price and credentials are favourable, you could write to him thus: "I am pleased to accept your quotation on the basis that all the following work is included:" and list the items agreed in your initial discussion. If the contractor accepts your letter without query, you can consider the work to be part of your 'contract', although it would be prudent to ask the contractor to acknowledge receipt of your letter.

Appendix 3 provides some technical information on a variety of types of work. Bear in mind that any preferences that a contractor expresses, for brands of equipment, types of material, etc., may be the result of experience or based on what he can obtain for the lowest price. Do not be afraid to tell one contractor the views of another and, where appropriate, speak to merchants and manufacturers to verify what you have been told. Be persuaded by reasoned argument. Be wary of "Naah, that's rubbish!"

'EXTRAS'

A primary cause of rocketing costs is the need for additional work that was not included in the contractor's price. This issue is discussed in Chapter 10 but may be distilled in the following key points:

● Try to consider, before you engage the contractor, what may be affected by the work and how it may escalate.
● Ask contractors – "What else may conceivably need to be done to complete the job?"
● Word your list of requirements in the broadest terms using phrases like "carry out all necessary work to ..." and "include all necessary making good". Ensure that the quotations refer to your list of requirements.
● Unless the work required is simple and clear cut, agree a method of pricing any additional work before you select your contractor.

If you are unsatisfied with some element of the work, withhold payment, or an appropriate proportion, until a suitable resolution has been offered. Paying the bill or signing a 'satisfaction note' (which some contractors may require) does not take away your rights as a consumer in respect of the supply of goods and services, but getting money back is not always easy. Pursue the contractor if you discover any defects after completion. Chapters 11, on payment and 12 on disputes will be useful if you have problems here.

Chapter 2:

Project Management – its Principles and Applications

It would be nice if we could just open our doors to a contractor and leave him to it, in the knowledge that we will get precisely what we want, or what is needed, for the price agreed. Unfortunately, life is seldom that simple and the essence of this book is that it's dangerous to hand over complete control when your wallet and your comfort are at stake.

So how do you keep in control? The answer is to be clear about what you want and, once the contractor has started work, to keep abreast of what is going on.

Being your own project manager

'Management' may have as many definitions as there are books on the subject, and it is clearly the conviction of some that it simply means ordering people about. Project management is far less about "direction" (to put it more politely), than about planning and monitoring. It centres around three core issues: quality, cost and time, because a successful project is one that delivers a quality product, within budget and on time. Even with large building projects the contractor knows broadly what he has to do so the job of the project manager is to ensure that everything is proceeding according to plan and that queries or problems are dealt with quickly.

Discussions with contractors and maybe a designer, together with guidance in this book, should help you to convert your initial thoughts into written requirements that contractors will understand. From this point, a process needs to be followed in order to achieve the desired outcome. These processes are broadly the same throughout the construction industry.

Project management and the construction industry: useful principles

The workings of major construction projects may be of marginal interest if you are just having your roof repaired but if you are planning something more substantial, there are a few important fundamentals that are worth understanding.

THE PARTIES INVOLVED

A client will engage an architect and various 'consulting engineers' to produce a design for the building and a project manager will be engaged to act as the client's 'agent' in managing the work. (The architect often takes on this role.)

In a major construction project there can be a huge number of different trades and specialists involved. If these trades were all employed separately by the client or project manager, the task of providing each with the correct information and coordinating their work would be a nightmare. Instead therefore, all the details required for the work (what is to be done and what materials are to be used) are incorporated into a single set of drawings and a written 'specification'. This package, together with information about the legal framework under which the construction work will be carried out, is then offered to a few selected large building contractors. The contractor with the preferred offer will be appointed as the 'main contractor' and this firm will employ all the other trades required. These are referred to as 'subcontractors' (their contracts are with the main contractor rather than with the client).

With this arrangement, as far as the client is concerned,

there is just one contractor (the main contractor) responsible for all elements of the work. Each subcontractor may employ his own specialists in the same way. Fig. 1 shows how an organisational chart of a typical project would look.

MANAGEMENT OF THE PROJECT

A programme of works is produced, usually by the main contractor, and shows in detail all the work involved and when it will be carried out. The quality of the work is monitored by the professional team, usually with assistance from a 'clerk of the works' (a kind of building site 'inspector' usually employed directly by the client). Project meetings are held throughout the contract, and are forums for discussion of quality, problems, changes and comparison of progress with the contractor's programme of works.

Any alterations or information not detailed in the specification are directed to the main contractor in writing, even if they are about work that has been 'subcontracted'. This ensures that the main contractor always knows what is going on. Costs are managed by quantity surveyors (the construction industry's accountants), and if changes have a cost implication they will agree or argue about the effect on the contract price.

PAYMENT

For projects that take several months to complete, the quantity surveyors agree the value of the work – usually monthly – so that the contractor may be paid in stages through the length of the project.

The professional team will be paid fees according to the value of the work, of which the bulk may be paid on completion of the design.

FINAL PAYMENTS

Final payments, which are sometimes more of a financial settlement, are generally paid after deducting a small

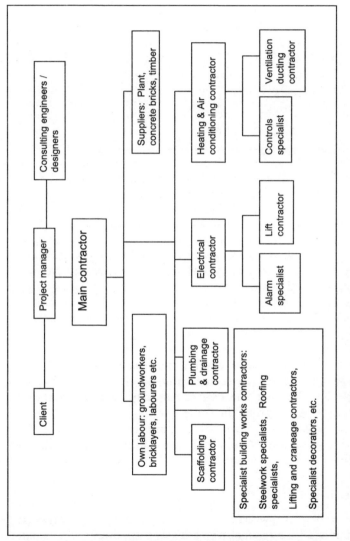

Fig 1 Organisation of a typical construction project

'retention' as a lever to encourage the contractor to fix any outstanding items or make good any repairs due to faulty workmanship. If the contract has not been completed on time, the client may be able to deduct 'damages' from payments to the contractor as compensation for any losses incurred through the delay.

There are variations on most elements of this process, the most notable being 'design and build' projects whereby the main contractor employs the designers.

The principles are, however, common throughout the industry and the same protocols will generally apply to domestic projects.

Applying the principles to domestic work

Defining exactly what work is required is crucial and, as mentioned, Chapter 6 covers this.

Once the contractor starts work you will have to assume to some degree that he knows what he is doing but you need not remain entirely in the dark. Familiarise yourself with the various steps or processes involved in the work by discussing work sequence and methodology with competing contractors and by going through each phase of the work with the appointed contractor before he starts. Remain aware of what needs to happen next, who needs to be around to do it and check progress with whatever programme has been agreed.

The one issue that you might feel unqualified to deal with is quality. The extent to which you can be an inspector of quality will be limited but having the confidence to ask questions can make all the difference. I shall cover this in due course.

Management of your building contract will require you to:

- *Understand* the processes involved and the order in which things need to be done.
- *Check* that they are done according to plan (the specification/brief and the programme).

- *Ensure* that everyone involved knows how their bit of the puzzle fits in with everyone else's.
- *Help* to resolve any problems as they arise.
- *Instruct* the contractor, in plenty of time, if changes are required.
- *Maintain* control of the finances.
- *Pay* the contractor periodically amounts commensurate with the work completed.

And, if you sense that things are not going well:

- *Intervene*, as soon as possible, to put things back on course.

The start to finish processes that will be required for all but the simplest of works will be:

1. Produce a detailed list of the work that you want done or your desired outcomes.
2. Arrange for drawings and design where necessary*
3. Obtain any necessary approvals (Planning permission etc.).
4. Select contractors to price.
5. Obtain prices from contractors – modifying requirements as necessary.
6. Analyse quotations and select a contractor.
7. Talk through the job with the contractor before he starts and obtain a programme of works.
8. Monitor progress and quality.
9. Deal with any alterations or additions.
10. Make any progress payments.
11. Inspect completed works, get contractor to deal with any 'snags'.
12. Make final payment.

---

* The sequence may be altered if the contractor is to produce the drawings.

Chapter 3:

Before you do anything . . .

Before taking your ideas to anyone else, it's worth considering exactly what you want from the project, e.g. more space? Improved saleability? Greater comfort? Or simply to halt some deterioration?

The following points should help you to think your ideas through in detail and alert you to some other things that may be involved in the project.

Is it practical? Is it worthwhile?

- *Extensions and major improvements* can certainly increase the value of a property but it is not always possible to fully recoup the costs when the property is sold. If a house is generally run down or in an undesirable location, an extension may add very little value. If your aim is to climb the property ladder, ask a local estate agent which improvements are likely to recover their costs or make a property more desirable.
- *Restoration* of a property to a period style, if increasing value, requires an eye for detail and a use of quality finishes. Tacky reproduction and (frequently out of character) moulded fitments can reduce the appeal of a property. There are some excellent books on this subject.
- *Double glazing* will generally have a payback of around 30+ years in terms of fuel saving (compared with 2-3

years for loft insulation* or 3-5 years for cavity wall insulation). It has become the norm as a home improvement because it has been heavily marketed. If you are tempted, do it for the right reasons: low maintenance (if using PVC-U or coated aluminium) and sound insulation. Double glazing may make the property more attractive to potential buyers although poorly chosen designs (e.g. PVC-U casements in a Victorian period dwelling) may have the opposite effect.

- *Internal partition changes* may have structural implications. Walls upstairs may need to be supported below. Consider the 'desirability' aspect: creating an extra bedroom by turning one nice-sized bedroom into two large cupboards is unlikely to be appealing to would-be purchasers. Turning a bedroom into an en-suite bathroom may reduce the value of the property. Be prepared to undo this type of work if you decide to sell. Structurally, not everything is possible – compromises may be necessary.

- *Consider the desirability of any extension.* Will it be a useful enhancement to the property? For example, will it take up too much of the garden? (Planning regulations may prohibit this in any case.) Will adding a further 2 metres onto an already sizeable living room warrant the cost? Will it make the room to which it is attached too dark? Adding an extra bathroom on the end of a kitchen would not be desirable or very practical. Adding a dining room or TV lounge onto the end of a kitchen is not a good idea either. (It is generally better to move the kitchen into the extension so that people don't have to traipse past the cook as they come and go.)

- *How will it affect the overall appearance of the property?* A tasteful extension, thoughtfully executed, can be of

---

*   250mm loft insulation where there is none at present

great value but an incongruous eyesore may make the property difficult to sell (see Chapter 5 – Planning, page 51).

What else may be affected? – Things that affect other things

Think carefully about whether the work you are planning would affect something else that is not intrinsically part of the works. For example, with a new extension: What's outside? Is there a tree in the garden? Does it have a preservation order? Is there a manhole out there?

EXTERNAL TERRAIN

A tree may be far enough away from the house not to be a problem, but it could affect the ground around an extension. Some trees, combined with certain soil types, may affect the ground up to 30 metres away.

Different soil types absorb moisture at different rates and foundations need to be designed to deal with this. Do not allow a designer or contractor simply to use the depth or design of the existing foundations to determine what may be needed for an extension.

New constructions adjacent to buildings with basements (yours or your neighbours) will need special consideration.

The existing foundations and structure must be checked if additional load is to be added, for example, if you intend to add a first floor extension over an existing ground floor extension.

EXISTING WATER AND ELECTRICAL SERVICES – OUTSIDE

Extensions must not cover up manholes below floors or access covers on vertical pipes. Rather than having a manhole under the carpet in your new dining room it is better to have the drain re-routed and the manhole repositioned so that it remains outside the house (see Fig. 2f on page 32). Identify where the existing pipes run and how they interconnect: open up the existing manholes and get someone to flush the loos and to open taps while you watch the waterflow. Any new connection will normally need to be via a manhole (see Appendix 3) and connected at 90° or greater to the existing pipework in the direction of flow – see Fig 2 overleaf. (See Appendix 3 for general layout of a plumbing system.)

If it is difficult to connect rainwater from an extension to the existing drainage, consider a 'soakaway'*.

> * A soakaway may be a purpose made tank buried in the ground or a large hole that is capped and filled with gravel. Its aim is to accept a large volume of water which gradually soaks into the adjacent soil. The size of the hole will be relative to the amount of water being discharged into it (i.e. size of roof = likely amount of rain falling on it) and the absorption rate of the subsoil. A soakaway must be a sufficient distance from the property to avoid damage to the foundations.

Damaging gas and water pipes can be expensive. Damaging electrical cables can be fatal! Approximate locations of existing services can be obtained from the local supply authorities. If you propose to build an extension over a 'public drain', e.g. one that takes waste from other dwellings as well, you will need permission from the local water authority. This can be complex and you may need to engage a suitable solicitor or surveyor to assist in this.

EXISTING WATER AND ELECTRICAL SERVICES – INSIDE

If you are extending the property substantially or adding an extra bathroom, check that the existing boiler and hot water cylinder is large enough to cope with the extra demand. Consider waste water from baths, WCs, etc. If all your waste plumbing is on the opposite side of your house to your proposed new bathroom, things will be complicated. The options

**DRAINAGE FROM A TYPICAL
'SEMI' WITH A REAR EXTENSION**

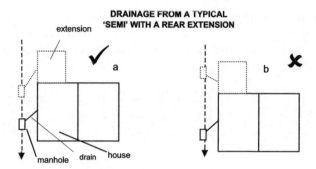

A new drain from an extension to a new (or existing) manhole must
connect in the direction of the water flow, as indicated by arrow

**DRAINAGE FROM A TYPICAL TERRACED
HOUSE WITH A REAR EXTENSION**

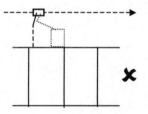

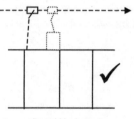

c Where it is not possible to
connect to an existing
manhole with a bend of
greater than 90°...

d ...it would be better to
add a new manhole to
the extension

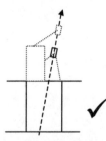

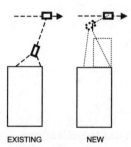

EXISTING   NEW

e Above is the suggested
arrangement where
the water flow runs
underneath the house

f Where an extension is to be
constructed over a manhole
location, the manhole should be
moved to a new location.

**Fig 2 Extensions – connecting to existing drainage via existing or new
manholes. (New extensions/drains/manholes shown dotted.)**

are either installing a new waste 'stack' and connecting to a drain, or pumping the waste to an existing waste stack*. With a new ground floor WC a route to the existing drainage may be found below the floor.

> * It is possible to install a WC and basin or even a complete bathroom at a distance from existing waste services by incorporating a special pump unit. *"Sani-flow"* is the lead manufacturer of these devices and this name has become generic (like Hoover). This really should be a last resort because no mechanical devices are trouble or maintenance free and the maintenance is not pleasant – a little imagination will explain what I mean.

New lighting and power sockets will generally just be added to the appropriate ring main, but for a sizeable extension a new circuit may be required. If you are adding a new electrical appliance such as an electric cooker or an immersion heater – anything over 3kw – it will need a separate circuit. In both cases, check that there is sufficient spare capacity on your existing fuse box or 'consumer unit' for an additional circuit. If your existing wiring is in poor condition, an electrician may refuse to add to it or modify it, so you may need to budget for re-wiring.

MAINTAINING SERVICES

If you are having new heating, plumbing, electrical work or a new kitchen installed where the work straddles several days, you may need to make some temporary arrangements. Discuss the effect on essential services with your contractor.

INTERNAL BATHROOMS

New internal bathrooms must be ventilated by fitting an extract fan controlled by the light switch or a 'passive infra-red' movement detector. The extract fan should have a 'run-on timer' so that it keeps running for a while after the room is vacated. The fan discharge will need to be ducted to outside, but a plastic pipe or a duct at high level in the corner of a bedroom doesn't look too good – therefore, some form of boxing may be required. The correct fan must be selected to suit the size of the room and the length of any discharge ducting. There must be a route for fresh air to enter the bathroom/WC. Under the door is usually adequate provided the door connects to a ventilated area (not a kitchen).

LOFT CONVERSIONS

Not every loft can be converted into a habitable space that is acceptable within Planning and Building Regulations. The height of the space, construction of the roof, thickness of the joists and where to put a staircase are the first things to be considered.

It's worth looking around locally at houses like yours with loft conversions, to see how they were done and which layout seems to work best. Most neighbours will be happy to show theirs off. With poorly designed (or not designed) loft conversions, the doors collide or resemble kissing gates and to get safely up or down the stairs you often need crampons and a good rope!

Loft conversions add an additional storey to a house and this increases the risk to life in the event of a fire. The local authority Building Control department (see Chapter 5, page 53) is responsible for policing fire regulations and, in order to comply, it will be necessary to provide sprung-closers to doors on escape routes, smoke detection and an escape window. If you intend to place your children at the top of the house, make sure they can hear an alarm and know how to get out.

Something will need to be done with the water tanks. If there is sufficient remaining loft space to the sides of the new rooms, they can be moved there but adequate access must be allowed so that a ball valve can be changed without making a hole in one of the new walls. Alternatively, everything could be fed directly from the cold water main (see Appendix 3) but no storage means no water at all in the event of mains water failure. If hot water is currently provided by a hot water cylinder fed from a tank that needs to be removed, the alternatives are:

a)   Fit a small tank (114 litre) just above the cylinder (although this will reduce the pressure available at the taps and may make showers impossible without a pump).

b)   Replace the existing cylinder with an 'unvented' cylinder which can be fed from the cold water main (expensive but practical).

c)   Change your boiler to a 'combination boiler' (see Heating – Appendix 3).

d)   Use a multipoint water heater (another box on the wall that requires a gas or electric supply).

If you have a small tank in the loft that feeds the heating system, there will probably be space for this but the tank must be higher than any radiators by at least 600mm. Alternatively, convert the heating system to a 'sealed system'. This is easy enough if the boiler is a recent model but an old boiler may not be suitable – in which case it could do with replacing anyway (Building Regulations may require the controls to be upgraded as well). This is a good example of how things can get more complicated than first envisaged.

CONVERTING A GARAGE INTO A HABITABLE ROOM

This may seem a very simple way to gain extra space but it is invariably more complicated than removing the doors, blocking up the wall, fitting a window and plastering. The garage may only have single skin walls – with inadequate thermal insulation and insufficient protection against dampness. Any external roof and the floor slab will also be uninsulated. To insulate the walls you could have an insulated timber stud wall on the inside or add thick proprietary insulating boards, but these will reduce the size of the room. With the possibility that rather than 'conversion' the job is actually 'demolition and rebuild' you should also check that the local Planning office will not refuse Planning permission on the basis that the garage constitutes a mandatory off street parking space.

WORK OUTSIDE THE CONTRACT (CONTRACTORS SIDE BY SIDE)

If you think it may be preferable or cheaper to exclude some element of the work from the building contract and have this done separately or to employ all the trades individually, think about how the work will be co-ordinated.

Having two or more contractors working in the same area under separate contracts is the bête-noire of the construction industry. Delays by one contractor can result in claims for additional costs by another and responsibilities may be unclear. With little technical knowledge, it may be difficult for you either to co-ordinate several contractors or arbitrate if there is any disagreement between them. It has even been known for separate trades to sabotage each other's work – just for a laugh! All these problems inevitably cost the client more.

If you nevertheless decide to separate out some part of the work, make sure that your principal contractor is happy with the arrangement and ensure that all parties speak to each other about all the details.

SECURITY

If a new flat roof will allow access to first floor rooms, those rooms will now require the same precautions as a ground floor room. Consult your insurers. If you are having an extension built, it is important that the new extension is secure before the 'knock through' into the main house is carried out.

YOUR HEALTH

If you or your partner are of 'a nervous disposition', think carefully before having major work done to your home. A little stress is rarely fatal but unless you have actually seen a building site transformed into a tidy home, midway through the construction of a sizeable extension, this may seem an impossible outcome. Living with builders, mess, dust and numerous other inconveniences is not easy for any of us and for someone who suffers from severe depression or anxiety it could push them over the edge. Keeping control of the project so that you know what to expect will make things easier but you must be prepared for some disruption.

Is it legal? – Who might have a say in what you do

RESTRICTIONS IMPOSED BY LEASES, DEEDS, LOANS OR INSURANCE

If you are a leaseholder your lease may detail what repairs you are responsible for and the extent to which you may be able to carry out any alterations. If in any doubt speak to the freeholder or, ultimately, a solicitor.

Alteration to some property is prohibited by a 'Restrictive Covenant' which will form part of the deeds. This may have been a condition of the original development when the property was built – possibly due to the Planning regulations of the time. This will need to be investigated and a solicitor, surveyor or architect with Planning knowledge may be required.

Some mortgage lenders may require notification of any proposed major work.

Tell your insurers before any work starts. Although your premium may be unaffected, your property might not be insured if there is a claim whilst the work is in progress.

BOUNDARIES

If boundaries around your property are indistinct, check that you will not be infringing on someone else's land or on a public right of way. Check deeds and Land Registry documents to determine the correct boundary location. Drawings that accompany deeds are usually to a very small scale so where accurate measurements are required, for example if you are building right to the boundary line, involve the owner of the neighbouring property and formally agree the precise boundary line with the assistance of a solicitor, surveyor or architect.

PLANNING AND BUILDING REGULATIONS, ETC.

Many types of work require approval from the local authority to ensure compliance with Planning, listed buildings and construction regulations. Failure to comply can lead to heavy fines and even a court order to modify or demolish. This subject is dealt with in Chapter 5.

PARTY WALLS

Party walls are those that divide two properties, typically between two halves of a 'semi' or each side of a terraced house. The 1996 "Party Wall etc. Act" defines the rights and obligations of the owners of each adjoining property. The Act also applies to boundaries between floors (in flats) and covers work adjacent to a boundary. Each owner has a right to carry out modifications such as thickening, cutting joists into or underpinning a party wall but he must serve a notice to the owner of (and anyone else having an interest in) the adjacent property before the work is carried out. A notice must also be served if it is proposed to carry out any excavation work (which can include the construction of a below ground drain) where:

a)   The work is below the level of the foundations of any neighbouring building within 3 metres, or

b)   Below the level of a 45 degree line taken from the point where the outside face of the neighbour's wall meets the bottom of his foundations and within 6 metres. See Fig. 3.

In all cases the person having the work done will be responsible for any damage caused to the neighbouring property as a result of the work.

Acknowledgement and acceptance of the notice will be required from your neighbour. No reply is taken as dissent and a party wall surveyor must be appointed to make an 'award' (an agreement whereby the work may proceed in a prescribed manner that protects the neighbour's interests and defines responsibilities).

Your neighbour may wish to employ his own surveyor and a third surveyor may need to be appointed as an arbitrator, all of which can get very expensive. It is possible for both you and your neighbour to use a single 'agreed surveyor' in order to minimise costs. If you are already employing a suitable surveyor, it is important to note that if he is appointed to deal with the matter under the Act, his first duty becomes that of an arbitrator rather than being your 'agent'.

Once a surveyor is appointed he can inspect the adjoining property and produce a 'schedule of condition' (a defects list detailing existing cracks, etc.) so that any existing problems are not blamed on the new work. The party having the work done pays the bill.

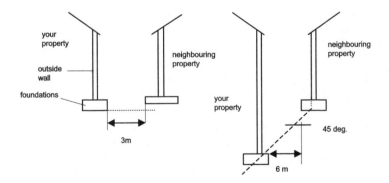

Fig 3 Three metre and six metre rules

Is it neighbourly? – What will the neighbours think?

If changes to your property are likely to affect your neighbours' enjoyment of their living space they may be able to
object during the Planning approval process. Creating
shade, blocking out light to windows, or overlooking a
neighbour's property are the most common problems.
Think carefully about what you are proposing and how you
might feel if you and your neighbour's roles were reversed,
then talk your plans through with them to obtain their
co-operation and avoid delays.

If you are extending your property along the party wall
line the requirements of the Party Wall etc. Act must be
adhered to (see above).

The ownership of a fence may be indicated in the deeds,
otherwise the general rule is that the owner of the fence has
the support posts on his side. When replacing a fence it is
worthwhile advising your neighbour beforehand and if he
happens to have climbing plants fixed to it, maybe working
together to remove the old one.

Can you afford it? – The budget and the funding

This may seem too obvious to mention but before you
engage a contractor to carry out any substantial works, you
must be sure that you can afford it.

Think about:

When the funds need to be available – is notice required,
for example from a savings account?

Does the lender need to inspect the works before releas-
ing funds? In this case get an undertaking that they will act
swiftly to avoid a delay in paying the contractor.

What monies need to be allocated to things you are
paying for yourself? For example, local authority approvals,
special materials.

Does the lender require you to engage a professional
designer and/or use a formal written contract?

In case unforeseen extra work becomes necessary, it is

worth having some 'contingency' sum available (although this is less likely to be necessary with 'packaged' work like double glazing or central heating).

If you are considering having the work done through a finance arrangement with the contractor, be sure to shop around to compare the costs of their finance – see Chapter 8 "Buying on credit", page 94.

Do you need an architect/surveyor/designer?

> Should you end up in court with a contractor, after his sketch concept of a loft conversion manifests itself as a dreadful eye-sore and you insist that you 'trusted the contractor's experience', a judge may rule that your trust was simply misplaced. Provided the contractor had not promoted his services as a designer, he may have no case to answer.

DESIGN

For most heating, plumbing, roofing, glazing and basic building works, a good contractor should have sufficient experience and technical knowledge to carry out the work without the need to involve a designer. However, where layout considerations, structural design, Building Regulations and quality finishes are involved, few contractors will have all the necessary skills and knowledge (even if they think they do). In these cases you should engage a suitable professional to produce the design or, in the case of minor works having design implications, at least provide details and any necessary drawings (more on this later).

Some contractors offer a 'Design and Build' service and it is important, if you are considering this option, to differentiate real D & B contractors from those who are happy to 'have a go' at the design (see above)!

EMPLOYING A SEPARATE PROJECT MANAGER

If you are undertaking a complex project and, having read this book you are not confident that you can keep track of all the issues involved, consider employing a project manager. Most architects will provide this service if required. On any substantial contract where there is no one living at the property to inspect the work regularly, this would be a sensible option. Complete reliance on someone else will always carry its risks, so check occasionally that the project manager is doing his job correctly.

Whether or not you intend to use a professional to help you, maintaining control means not underestimating the amount of close involvement in the project that will be required of you. For example, you may wish to avoid undertaking a major project at home when you are also under pressure at work!

Most of the issues in this chapter should arise when you discuss your plans with a designer or contractor, but that cannot be guaranteed. To avoid nasty surprises, inaccurate budget figures or even claims for additional work, try your best to think of everything and not rely entirely on those you employ.

What is the first step? – The design and tendering process

The route you take between committing your initial thoughts to paper and getting a contractor on site will depend on your abilities and the complexity of the work. Fig. 4 shows the options.

If you intend to engage an architect or surveyor to do the design work, you should produce an 'outline brief' from which that professional can work (see Chapter 6). Once the design is completed and any Planning or Building Control approval received, either you or your designer will need to invite prices from contractors based on the design. A 'Design and Build' contractor (see Chapter 4, page 48) will also require an outline brief.

For more routine work, where no designer is involved, you should produce a fully detailed brief against which contractors can offer a price. You may wish to discuss the work with a few contractors before you finalise this (see Chapter 6, page 64).

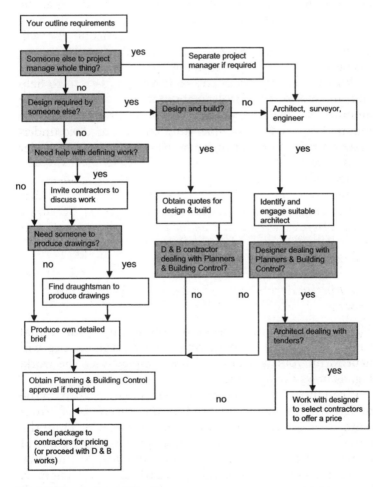

Fig 4 Design and supply routes

Chapter 4:

Construction Design

Construction professionals

Professional drawings should be produced for any substantial work, and may be required for Planning and Building Control approval. Extensions built without plans frequently include poor construction methods or hideous detailing. If a contractor advises that, for any substantial work, a drawing is unnecessary – find another contractor. The type of professional you engage to produce drawings will depend on the scale of the work. Outlines of various professionals' roles are given below.

DRAUGHTSMEN AND DESIGNERS

A draughtsman may have sufficient skills to produce drawings for smaller work (e.g. showing a revised elevation for converting a garage into a room for Planning consent), but may lack detailed knowledge of Building Regulations or structural engineering. Such a person would be inappropriate for major alterations or extensions. Interior and landscape designers clearly have their own fields of expertise and can be employed directly or by an architect if their work is to be incorporated into a wider project. Local newspapers and Yellow Pages carry advertisements for draughtsmen and designers.

ARCHITECTURAL DESIGN

A good architect will have a vast knowledge of building matters including Building Regulations, construction materials and an understanding of appropriate style and detailing. This knowledge can sometimes help to create a less expensive design than contractors alone may achieve using only materials and methods that are familiar to them. It can also mean that staircases and doorways are designed to be wide enough to fit your furniture through and you don't bang your head on the ceiling when you go up the stairs!

An architect will generally produce drawings and a detailed specification against which to obtain competitive prices from contractors. Architects can provide a range of service options including obtaining and appraising tenders and project management.

The Royal Institute of British Architects (see Appendix 7 for details) will have details of suitable architects in your area and produces a useful guide called "Engaging an Architect". Architects are also listed in Yellow Pages.

STRUCTURAL DESIGN

Structural engineering is the design of a structure so that it will not fall down or move unduly. Cracks appearing in corners, around structural members or where an extension joins the existing building can be a sign of poor structural design.

Extension work and some internal partition changes will have structural implications. If you are also using an architect he may engage a structural engineer on your behalf. Alternatively, you could engage the engineer separately as you may for the design of a single beam or to inspect a structural defect. Good contractors may be capable of selecting standard structural members but even with minor structural work, a visit by a structural engineer and some useful guidance could be money well spent. Structural calculations may be required by the Building Control officer and an engineer will be required to do this. Structural engineers may be found in the Yellow Pages or through their professional body; the Institution of Structural Engineers (address in Appendix 7).

SURVEYORS

The term 'surveyor' covers a wide range of construction 'specialists' and there is some overlap with work done by architects. Surveyors will generally have good knowledge of construction issues and may be perfect for routine alterations and advice on repairs. Party wall surveyors are specially qualified to act in this capacity. Architects may have more flare where there is a variety of design options and may be more creative with internal layouts, external features and composition.

The Royal Institute of Chartered Surveyors (see Appendix 7 for contact details) is the professional body for surveyors and it will have details of appropriate and qualified surveyors in your area.

Selecting and hiring the right professionals

It is important to select a professional who is familiar with the type of work that you require: an architect who specialises in designing factory buildings is unlikely to be the best person to design your extension. It can also be useful to select designers who are familiar with the idiosyncrasies of your local Planning and Building Control officers. Whether you just need drawings or a full design, select a designer with whom you can have a good working relationship – you may need to speak to more than one. The better the mutual understanding, the more likely it is that your vision of what you want will be accurately reflected in their design.

Recommendation is the best source of a suitable professional; otherwise consult the appropriate professional body. If you are simply selecting from a list it would be wise to ask for a couple of references and a sample drawing. Check, with referees, that:

- There were few queries about the drawings from either Planning or Building Control officers.
- The contractors, when they carried out the work, could easily understand what was required.

- There were few alterations or changes made as a result of details not being shown on the drawings.
- There were no serious arguments between client, architect and contractor.
- There were few extra costs due to changes made by the architect once the work had started.

Sample drawings should be neat and easy to read. They should be fully dimensioned with necessary elevations, copious notes detailing materials to be used and large scale views and sections to show intricate details.

It is essential to know what any professional will and will not be responsible for – and liable for if something goes wrong. Use the following checklist. Who will be responsible for:

1. Structural integrity of the building / engaging a structural engineer?
2. Overall building design and materials specification?
3. Dealing with external matters e.g. drainage / surveying external services?
4. Dealing with plumbing and electrical work?
5. Dealing with Planning permission (if applicable)?*
6. Dealing with Building Control approval?*
7. The tender process?
8. Managing the project – checking quality, costs and progress?
9. Inspecting the work to confirm completion in accordance with the contract?
10. If project management is not included will they visit the site, occasionally or at all, during the work to check that the work is proceeding according to plan?

When you have established what elements your professional

---

* Obtaining permission will remain your responsibility, but a professional can be of great assistance with the process.

or professionals will be responsible for, this must be agreed and laid down in writing together with an outline of the work required. Your professional will work against this 'brief'. It is important to get this right. Most of the professional bodies produce standard 'terms of engagement' for the scale of work proposed – alternatively an exchange of letters detailing respective responsibilities would usually suffice. Fees will be dependent on the level of service required and the value of the work involved.

If dealing with Planning and Building Control officers is part of the remit, the professional should allow for necessary discussions and minor modifications to drawings. 'Difficult' council officers can lead to requests for additional fees.

Taking the 'design and build' route

Where design input and drawings are required, the simplest option may appear to be to engage a contractor who will do the whole thing for you. Some construction firms specialise in domestic extensions and employ architects and engineers so that they can offer the whole package. They may also deal with Planning permission and Building Control approval.

This option is clearly attractive but some caution is required. Having all contractors tendering against the same design ensures, as much as is possible, that all contractors are offering the same job. If they are designing the work themselves, the lowest price may be due to a 'cheaper' design rather than a competitive price. Also, some 'design and build' contractors tend to crash on a bit and just give the client what they think he'll want, turning the construction of an extension into 'packaged' work like double glazing. An architect or surveyor would expect to spend time with his client when producing the design. If you choose the design and build route you need to be confident that the firm places the necessary emphasis on their responsibilities as designers. See also Comparing Design & Build Proposals – Chapter 8, page 91.

Design and build contractors should be asked to provide with their prices an outline specification indicating, in broad terms, the standard of materials and of detailing that would be employed. A copy of a drawing and specification for similar work would also be helpful to aid comparison.

D & B contractors may list themselves in the Yellow Pages under "Extensions", but recommendations are a better way to find them.

Chapter 5:

Local Authority Approvals

There are two entirely separate local authority departments who may have an interest in work that you are proposing to do on your property: 1. The Planning Department (which grants 'Planning permission') and 2. The Building Control Department (which issues 'Building Control Approval'). It is important to understand the requirements of these authorities. Even when a designer is involved with a project, you will be the 'applicant' for the purposes of obtaining approvals. Given that both procedures can involve a degree of negotiation though, it is wise to ask your professionals to deal with the appropriate council officers directly.

1. Obtaining Planning permission

Planning regulations are introduced by central government and enforced by local authorities. They are a balance between protection of amenity and the environment on the one hand and the freedom of the individual to develop and improve property where desired, on the other.

If your property is occupied by a single family, the likelihood of you requiring Planning permission is largely dependent upon the relationship between the proposed alteration or addition and the size and location of the existing property. With 'multiple occupancy' dwellings, permission will be required for any material alterations to the external appearance. The main situations where Planning permission is required are outlined in Appendix 4 but rules are applied differently across the country, and some local authorities have their own special requirements.

PERMITTED DEVELOPMENT (PD)

Extensions or additions to single family dwellings, not exceeding the area or dimensional constraints mentioned in Appendix 4 may fall within the scope of 'Permitted Development', in which case Planning permission is not required. In some areas though, local authorities have had permitted development withdrawn due to particular local requirements and if your property has an existing extension, some PD may already be used up. Internal layout changes do not require Planning permission unless the property is 'listed as being of special architectural or historical interest' in which case Listed Buildings Consent will be required.

Do not go by what your neighbours or friends have or have not done. Rules differ from area to area and some people break the rules in ignorance. At worst, this can result in having to take down what you have built and, at your own expense, restore everything to the way it was before.

For any work involving extending or changing the appearance of your property, visit the Planning Department to obtain advice or send a set of existing and proposed drawings and ask whether permission is required. State whether the property is flats or a 'single family dwelling'. Where permission is not required, you can obtain a 'certificate of lawful proposed development' as written confirmation, but this may take longer.

DESIGN GUIDELINES

Additions to a property should be carried out in a way that is sympathetic to the design of the existing structure, and this may be a condition of some Planning requirements. Fig. 5 (overleaf) illustrates some do's and don'ts.

PLANNING APPLICATIONS

If Planning permission is required (as per guidelines in Appendix 4, page 195), an application form will need to be

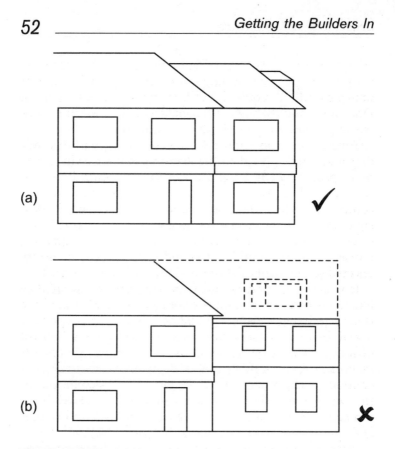

(a)

(b)

Fig 5 Good and bad design

Hopefully the difference will be obvious. With (a) above, the proportion of the extension to the original house, the roof design, the window sizes and detailing is all in harmony with the original house so that it looks like it could have been built at the same time. The brickwork, window sills etc. should also match.

With (b) all these points are ignored and it looks awful. Extensions or dormer windows to hipped roofs should be hipped to match with a pitch of the same angle: gable ends or flat roofs should not be used. The Planning rules are generally less stringent for additions to rear elevations but poor design can affect the value of a property. In conservation areas the size and style of windows will be required to match the existing.

completed and sent to the Planning Department together with drawings. The Planning Office will advise what sort of drawings will be required and how many copies they need. Drawings should show sufficient detail for Building Control approval as well where this is required.

Your application should be acknowledged within a few days and will be placed on the Planning Register, which may be inspected by interested parties (usually including contractors looking for work). Your neighbours may also be contacted so that they can lodge any objections. Within eight weeks, unless you have agreed that the council may extend this period, permission should be either granted, refused or granted subject to conditions. If your plans are rejected you can appeal, but obtain specialist advice for this.

It is better to understand from the Planners what they like to see before you complete your plans, rather than have them rejected and require modification. If your property is 'listed' or in a 'conservation area' a Development Control officer may also be involved in the approval process. If Planning permission is being dealt with by a designer or a contractor, check regularly that the necessary communication with local authority departments is taking place. There can sometimes be a fine line between approval and refusal and some negotiation can tip the balance.

Planning officers will want to visit the property before, possibly during, and after completion of work. Notification will be required when the appropriate stages are reached. Make sure that your contractor complies precisely with approved drawings.

Once permission is obtained, you have five years in which to start the work. There is no time limit for completion.

2. Obtaining Building Control (Building Regulations) approval

The standard of building construction, compliance with Building Regulations and the Building Act, is controlled by the Building Control Department of the local authority in which the work is being carried out. The 'Building Regulations' indicate basic construction performance standards and methods of compliance are detailed in 13 'Approved Documents' (17 parts in Scotland) covering the various elements of building construction. Copies are available in most libraries (see also 'Resources' Appendix 7, page 217).

Building an extension, structural work such as moving or demolishing load bearing walls, moving or adding staircases, loft conversions and any work involving new foundations, structural design or drainage will all need Building Control approval.

Certain replacement and renovation work will also need to comply with the Building Regulations although specific approval is not required – see below. Under the regulations, an applicant has the choice of using one of two methods of applying for approval (also called 'consent').

1. BUILDING NOTICE

A building notice advises the Building Control Department that work will be carried out so that an inspector can visit the site during the work to ensure compliance with the regulations. You will need to complete a form giving details of the work proposed and if the work includes an extension or new building, the form must be submitted with a 'block plan'. This is a drawing to a scale of no smaller than 1:1250 showing the size and position of the building or the building as extended and its relationship to adjoining boundaries. Provision for drainage should also be shown. The inspector can request further drawings or calculations if he feels they are necessary.

2. FULL PLANS SUBMISSION

With the Full Plans method, the applicant demonstrates, by way of drawings, that the construction will comply with the regulations. A completed form and the following drawings will be required:

a) A location plan to a scale of no smaller than 1:1250 showing the building, the boundaries of the property in relation to adjacent streets and houses and any proposed extension or additional structure. An Ordnance Survey plan may be obtained from the council and marked up for this purpose.

b) Plans, sections and elevations together with technical notes that fully describe the proposed construction. A scale of 1:100 may be suitable but 1:50 drawings may be required in some cases.

c) Structural calculations, if the work involves any new or altered load bearing elements.

d) Proposals for building over or adjacent to any sewer – if applicable.

You can produce your own drawings but logically, in order to do so, you must have adequate construction knowledge. Generally, an architect, surveyor or suitable draughtsman will be required for this. The Building Control Department will usually issue a conditional approval notice, indicating any changes required although plans can be rejected. The work will still require inspection as it proceeds.

Whilst applicants can choose either method, for major works like extensions and loft conversions, the full plans method is preferable, because alterations needed to change anything that the inspector is not happy with inevitably cost money. For smaller structural works or drainage alterations, the building notice method may be adequate.

If work is carried out without Building Control consent, it is possible to obtain approval retrospectively by applying for a 'Regularisation Certificate'. Exposing foundations and possibly structural elements may be required and if work is found not to comply with regulations, remedial work will be required before a certificate is issued. Altogether the most expensive method of obtaining approval!

FEES

With Full Plans submission the fee is divided into a 'plan fee' which is payable on submission of the plans and an inspection fee which is payable after the first inspection.

With the building notice method, the two are combined and required on deposit of the application. Fees are based on the scale of the work but would be typically around £350 for an extension under 40 sq. metres in area. (2003 prices)

INSPECTIONS

With both methods, Building Control officers will want to inspect the works at the following stages (if relevant to the work being carried out).

a)   Excavation for foundations.
b)   Foundation concrete – before covering up.
c)   Damp proof courses.
d)   Oversite concrete.
e)   Drains – prior to covering up.
f)   Possibly, structural steelwork before covering up.

At least two days' notice must be given before commencement of work and at least one day's notice prior to any covering up. It is generally appropriate for the contractor to notify the Building Control office but it remains the client's project and the client's responsibility. These inspections need to be carried out both for peace of mind and to obtain final approval, without which the property may not reach its potential resale value.

RENOVATION AND REPLACEMENTS

If substantial work is carried out to the existing fabric or services, Part L of the regulations (Conservation of fuel and power) requires that element to be upgraded or rebuilt to comply with the current regulations. This specifically applies to:

- Replacement external doors, windows and roof lights.
- Replacement heating boilers and hot water storage vessels.
- Major work to: roofs, floors or walls.

These regulations apply from April 2002 and whilst no specific Building Control approval is required, contractors are expected to comply. Ultimately, responsibility rests with the building owner.

CONSERVATORIES

Conservatories must have glazing in accordance with Part N of the regulations. In order to comply with the requirements to conserve energy (Part L), conservatories should be separated from the remainder of the dwelling. If an existing opening is used to gain access to the conservatory, it must have the same standard of insulation / draft proofing as the rest of the house. If a new or enlarged opening is created, the new doors must comply with current Building Regulations.

Whether or not these latter items are adequately policed, the provisions will result in lower fuel bills, so it is worth ensuring that contractors comply.

Chapter 6:

Contracts, Specifications and Briefs

The 'contract'

For the same reasons that you don't want to become an expert in building construction to have an extension built, you probably don't want to be an expert in contract law to employ a builder. Nevertheless, some rudimentary knowledge of the legal relationships formed will be helpful.

Any arrangement that a homeowner makes with a contractor to carry out work will result in a legal contract provided:

a)   There is an 'agreement' between the parties that the work is to be carried out.

b)   There is a 'consideration' – a legal term meaning an exchange of promises: usually a service performed or work carried out in exchange for money.

c)   There is an 'intention' to be bound by the agreement. This means that both parties must intend to enter into an agreement.

These same basic 'rules of contract' apply to the purchase of anything from double-glazing to a can of beans. When buying a can of beans there is little opportunity for ambiguity with regard to the terms of the agreement, so a written contract is not required – just as well because the queues at supermarket checkouts are bad enough as they are!

The need for putting the details of any agreement into writing is directly proportional to its complexity and the potential for misunderstanding. If an item of work is easily identified, (e.g. a broken section of guttering), and you ask a builder to offer a price to fix it, your acceptance of that price constitutes a contract and there is little need for anything in writing. For a more complex job, verbal agreement or sealing the deal with a handshake may not afford either party sufficient protection if things go wrong.

The existence of a contract gives the parties certain rights and duties, which are enforceable in the courts. If either party fails to perform its obligations under the contract, he may be in 'breach' of the contract. The consequences of this are:

i)   The innocent party may seek 'damages' (compensation) for loss incurred because of the breach.
ii)   The innocent party may terminate the contract if the breach is serious, i.e. it is a breach of a fundamental element of the contract.
iii) The party who is in breach may be unable to enforce the contract against the innocent party.

IMPLIED TERMS

In addition to any terms that may be stated in writing or agreed verbally, the courts may decide that other clauses must be implied into the contract because they are an obvious requirement of the transaction. The most common source of these implied terms with contracts involving the individual emanates from consumer legislation. In particular, the various Sale of Goods Acts and the Trade Descriptions Act.

The essence of these pieces of legislation is that:

1.   Any goods (materials) shall be of a 'satisfactory' quality.
2.   Any goods (materials) must be as they are described in any offer.

3.   Work shall be carried out with 'reasonable care and skill'.
4.   Work shall be performed 'within a reasonable time'.

Words such as 'reasonable' and 'satisfactory' give the courts the latitude to judge whether a contractor is clearly trying to get away with something that he should not or if the consumer is being impossibly pedantic.

The above requirements may act as a useful safety net but most construction works really need something more akin to a harness, and a written contract focuses both parties more directly on their obligations.

Written contracts

There are no hard and fast rules about when construction work in the home requires a written contract. A lot of work is carried out without anything at all in writing beyond the contractor's quotation, but these seldom say anything about quality, how long the job may take or other issues that may be important to you.

For all commercial construction work, ready written contracts are used to define in great detail the responsibilities of the parties, and how to deal with issues such as alterations to the work, failure of the contractor to perform, etc.

There are various so-called 'Standard Forms of Contract' in general use throughout the construction industry, but few are suitable for use in domestic scale work.

The principal source of most building contracts is the Joint Contracts Tribunal (JCT) and it is possible, if you are discussing a fairly large project with a medium sized contractor, that he, or the architect, will suggest a JCT 'Minor Works' contract which will be suitable for works up to around £150,000.

With 'design and build' contracts, the contractor must take full responsibility for the design of the work in addition to the construction. The JCT 'Standard form of Building Contract with Contractors Design' provides for this.

The Federation of Master Builders produces a good contract for domestic work which has received the Plain English Campaign's 'Crystal Mark' for its readability by the non-lawyer. This, whilst being a fair document, is designed to be used by a contractor: so 'We' in the document means the contractor and 'You' means you the client. An even simpler document, in my view, is produced by the JCT and called the 'Building Contract for a Home Owner / Occupier'. This has also received the Plain English Crystal Mark and its simplicity would make it appropriate for most domestic work. The package includes two copies (one for the client and one for the contractor) of a contract form and a set of conditions. It is available at a moderate price from RIBA Publications (address in Appendix 7).

There are two elements to most contracts; the 'Contract Form', which is in the style of a typical agreement, and the 'Conditions'. In the case of contracts for larger projects, such as the JCT Minor Works contract, the conditions are rarely included with the documentation; rather they are simply referred to like a British Standard publication.

As an alternative to the above standard contracts, I have included in Appendix 1 some standard conditions that are suitable for a medium- to large-scale project and which you may copy into a document of your own if you feel that they are appropriate. These also give a flavour of the sort of terms you will find elsewhere. Most contract conditions are the result of some forethought and a lot of pooled bad experiences, so the clauses are also a useful indication of the areas within construction work where disputes can occur. For smaller jobs, the essence of appropriate clauses may be adapted into a simple letter that goes with your brief.

If you are likely to incur financial loss or severe inconvenience if work is not completed by a particular date, you could make completion before this date a condition of the contract. Adding the phrase "time is of the essence in this contract" to the conditions is the usual recommendation but this may still require you to sue the contractor for breach of contract if he fails to meet the date. A 'penalty

clause' (see Chapter 13, page 149) allows deductions from
the contract price to cover any loss and this may be more
straightforward. The difficulty will be finding a contractor
who is willing to accept either method.

Specifications

Many disputes in domestic construction work are about
what was supposed to be included in the contractor's price.
A detailed specification will avoid most of these problems
and ensure that all the tendering contractors are pricing for
the same thing. For any substantial construction work, an
architect or surveyor should be engaged to produce a design
and a specification which should include full details of the
work required and what materials should be used. Much of
this information will be put on to drawings, though some
separate text is usually advisable to explain workmanship
requirements. For your initial consultation with the
architect/surveyor, see below, under 'A brief for the
designer'.

   Where there is no designer involved, write down your own
detailed list of requirements against which the contractor
can offer a price. Unless you have sufficient construction
knowledge or are being closely advised by someone suitably
qualified, you should avoid using the word 'specification' in
this document. To produce a 'specification' is to 'specify'
and this has a particular connotation in the realms of
design responsibility which may cloud the issue in the event
of a dispute. You should call your document a 'brief' but
you should make it as detailed as possible – see below, under
'A detailed brief for a contractor'.

Producing a brief

A BRIEF FOR THE DESIGNER

Start by writing down a general outline of the work required
and then list any specific requirements to indicate how you

envisage the final work. Then choose your designer and work with him in producing an agreed brief that includes both details of the work and the services that you wish him to perform. Be prepared to revise your initial expectations and allow your designer's expertise to formulate the final work plan.

A DETAILED BRIEF FOR A CONTRACTOR

For more modest works where no designer is involved, you will need to submit to the contractor a detailed brief. Its scale will depend on the work involved but try to include as much detail as you can without going into details of construction methods (except where you are clear and confident that your requirements are appropriate).

A brief is essential to explain what you want and it is evidence of the standards that you expect – but it is important to make it clear that it is just your best attempt to convey your requirements. It should not absolve the contractor of his responsibility to use his own expertise to interpret your desires and use appropriate materials and methods. The general conditions shown in Appendix 1 highlight this responsibility on the part of the contractor.

In Appendix 3, I have provided a range of general construction notes from which you may wish to draw information. Use this, discussions with visiting contractors, manufacturers' specifications and your own feelings about how you want things to look to determine what you include in your brief. The more research you do about different materials, processes and equipment, the more you will be in a position to make your own decisions or at least discuss the work, authoritatively, with the contractor. Without this information you must rely entirely on his advice. Within Appendix 3, I have included, in bold type, some general clauses which, whilst non-specific in terms of material selection, specify minimum standards with which the work should comply. Appendix 2 shows a typical brief.

QUESTIONNAIRE

Where there is no designer, in order to check if lower prices are a result of inferior methods or materials, ask contractors to provide details of how they will do the work. Either produce a schedule that the contractor returns with his price or a simple list of questions that he can answer in his offer, e.g.

i)   What floor construction do you propose to use?
ii) What wall construction do you propose to use?
iii) What roof construction do you intend to use?
iv) How do you intend to connect the new garage to the existing wall of the house? Etc.

Explain that this is for the purposes of evaluating tenders so that your decision is not based on price alone.

DETAILS AND EXTENT OF WORK

Some items may require some ingenuity on the part of the contractor so highlight these items and ask, in the brief, for the contractor to discuss them with you. The phrase "Allow for all necessary work in connection with . . .." is useful and reduces the risk that the contractor will try to make an extra charge for something that is obviously required.

The aesthetics of the finished job will be what you see every day so think about how things should look. How will joints between different surfaces be treated? How will the ends of mouldings be treated (see Fig. 6)? If you are having shelving or cupboards built, consider what the fixings will look like. Try to visualise each element of the work and mentally zoom into each corner, each joint, each fitting of a piece of equipment and include requirements in your brief or discuss details with contractors. Never assume that the contractor will do everything to your liking.

People frequently think of some other piece of work when the job is half way through and contractors may suggest

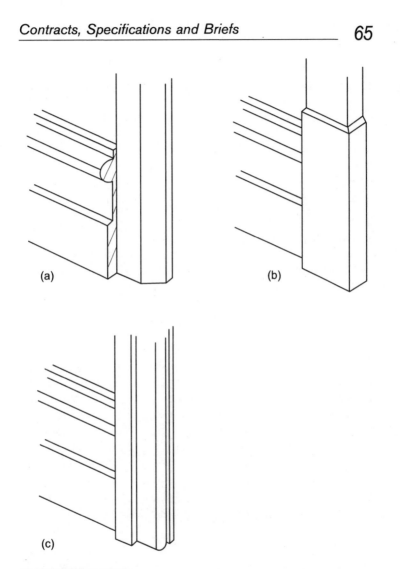

Fig 6 Moulding details

The 'raw edges' of mouldings should, where possible, be hidden. They should either abut a flat surface or other mouldings of appropriate size.

(a) above shows a period skirting abutting and overhanging a modern simple architrave. The same can happen with a poorly chosen dado rail.

(b) and (c) show better detailing; using either a 'plinth' against which the skirting can sit or as in (c) a more suitable moulding of larger section.

that something else 'might as well' be done at the same time. In both cases the result can be expensive 'extras'. Visualise the completed job and consider if it will make something else look odd or inappropriate. Make sure contractors understand what you want to achieve and ask them to make suggestions **before** you settle on the final scope of work.

SPECIAL PURCHASES AND DOING WORK YOURSELF

With items such as ironmongery, sanitaryware, taps, light fittings, etc., if you don't specify what you want, the contractor will probably supply the cheapest available. So do your own browsing and list details and catalogue numbers in your brief. If you intend to purchase items yourself, indicate, in the brief, that the contractor is to allow for fitting only. However, if you purchase items yourself and they are damaged, poorly made or the wrong size, it will be your problem – and if the contractor has to sort it out he may charge you for so doing. If the contractor supplies everything, it is the contractor's responsibility to sort out any problems within his price. The contractor's 'mark up' on the cost can hence be useful insurance. Any items that you supply yourself must be to hand when the contractor needs them. If any work is to be carried out by someone other than the principal contractor, the demarcation of responsibility must be made clear and co-ordination will be your responsibility. It will be essential that you understand the order in which work needs to be done for you to co-ordinate two or more trades.

PRELIMINARIES

Some considerations which are not part of the work itself may have a cost implication for the contractor. In larger contracts, these are referred to as 'preliminaries'. Examples are:

- 'Welfare' facilities – will there be access to the bathroom? If the work is largely external and you do not want muddy boots in the house, you may want the contractor to allow for a portable (chemical) toilet.

- Availability of a water supply – outside tap or access to house?
- Availability of electricity – access to the house, outside power point or a portable generator to annoy the neighbours? (Beware of the potential security risk with extension leads passed through open windows.)
- Storage of materials. You may need to allocate adequate space for this and if storage needs to be outside the house a secure and weatherproof container may be required.
- Protection/security of the site if the work will compromise this, e.g. removal of a boundary wall, scaffolding.

If any of the above requires equipment to be provided by the contractor, he must be advised of this before pricing.

If you intend to hold any retention or include any 'penalty clause' other than may be part of a recognised formal contract, you must include details with your documentation (see Chapter 13, page 149).

Tender documents

A weighty phrase if you are just having minor work done but for everything, except straightforward repairs, you should provide contractors with written information against which they can offer a price, and which will also determine the details of any subsequent contractual arrangement. The following is a checklist of the items required:

- ❑ A covering letter, which may refer to an earlier telephone call or maybe to a survey that the contractor has carried out (see sample letter 1 on page 205).
- ❑ Your designer's drawings and any separate specification OR your detailed brief.

❏ Details of any preliminary items. These may be included in your letter.

❏ Any other relevant information such as schedules of specified items, e.g. ironmongery.

❏ Details of the 'contractual terms' on which you will enter into an agreement, e.g. a specific pre-printed contract (as mentioned earlier) or your own set of conditions (e.g. as or based on my Appendix 1, page 154).

❏ Any questionnaire that you may wish the contractor to complete in respect of proposed construction details.

❏ A price summary (see below).

❏ A copy (unsigned) of any form of agreement that may be used with a pre-printed contract (if appropriate).

PRICE SUMMARY

With any substantial work, the contractor should be asked to break down his price. There are a number of reasons for doing this.

1) If the prices exceed your budget you might wish to omit some part of the work. If the item is priced separately, you will have the information on which to base a decision.

2) A price breakdown is very useful when analysing the competing prices; the lowest might not be the cheapest (see 'Comparing offers', Chapter 8, page 83)!

3) If different contractors allow for slightly different things – where you have not been specific in your requirements, you can compare these items separately and ask contractor B how his price would be affected if he used the materials or method suggested by contractor A.

4) It makes calculation of staged payments easier (see Chapter 11, page 121).

5) It makes pricing additional work easier. (see Chapter 10, page 112).

Where either a square metre or linear metre rate can be applied to the works, as with plastering, pointing, walling and piping etc., ask contractors to quote a rate in their offers. This will be useful if there are alterations or additions to the quoted work. Providing rates will be essential where elements of the work cannot be easily quantified in advance as, for example, with some restoration work.

Chapter 7:

Obtaining Prices from Contractors

Finding a contractor

The market place for all household service trades is the classified telephone directories and local press. But how do you choose? Well I'm sorry but there is no easy answer to this. My advice is to put the books to one side and ask everyone you know in the locality if they can recommend someone. You could also drive around your neighbourhood looking for houses where work is being carried out. The ubiquitous skip is a good clue. Most people are happy to share their experiences and personal recommendation is generally less likely to lead to disappointment – although it is no guarantee. If you are engaging professionals to do design work, ask them if they know of any suitable contractors, with whom they have worked and who have proved acceptable.

If you are unable to draw up a list of contractors from recommendations alone you will need to look to the market. For small jobs, check out the small or single line classified ads, which are usually individual tradesmen in business for themselves. When available, these may produce competitive prices. Beyond this, the advertisements themselves are little guide to the quality or size of the contractor. A professional looking ad does not mean that the firm advertising is 'professional'. It is easy for a complete fraud to look impressive in an ad – in fact it will be his speciality!

THE LOGOS

Many construction firms sport the logos of organisations to which they belong. Some are more useful than others in terms of providing consumer comfort.

Federation of Master Builders

A trade association. Member contractors must have been in business for at least 12 months, are required to provide references from six satisfied customers and are vetted by local branch members. The FMB operate a dispute resolution service and have a code of practice and complaints procedure to deal with client/contractor disagreements. Registered Warranted Builder members have to have been in business for at least three years and satisfy financial and public record checks as well as FMB's other entry requirements. They can offer the MasterBond 10 year insurance backed warranty on building projects for an insurance premium of 1.5% of the cost of the work (plus insurance premium tax).

Guild of Master Craftsmen

A trade association covering a range of industries. Members are expected to provide references from previous customers.

League of Professional Craftsmen

The League of Professional Craftsmen is a trade association dedicated to promoting businesses where a high degree of skill or expertise is required. In a nutshell the League exists to protect the public by separating the skilled from the unskilled.

CORGI

Council for Registered Gas Installers (CORGI)

CORGI is not a trade association, but is a body approved by the Health & Safety Executive and given the responsibility for maintaining a register of competent, qualified gas installers. By law, registered installers must be qualified (by examination) in terms of both knowledge and technical skill in relation to gas work. Registered installers that employ operatives must ensure that the operatives are competent to carry out gas work and hold current qualifications for the categories of work they are employed in. Registration can be removed for serious breach of gas safety regulations. Any contractor you use for work on gas pipes or gas appliances must be CORGI registered. (This includes operatives fitting gas cookers in fitted kitchens.) Registered installers carry a credit card style ID card. It is not a legal requirement for operatives running heating pipework or fitting radiators, etc. to a gas fired heating system to be CORGI registered provided they do not work on the gas part of the system. It may be argued though that in most cases registration is an indication of general competence.

ECA

Electrical Contractors' Association (ECA)

A trade association whose members have been assessed to ensure that they are technically competent and that their work complies with the wiring regulations and relevant standards and codes of practice. Members can offer an insurance backed warranty on installation work and a bond scheme that ensures work is completed if the member should go bust. The Association provides training for members and provides certification documents for the inspection and testing of electrical installations.

National Inspection Council for Electrical Installation Contracting (NICEIC)

Approved contractors need to have been trading for at least 12 months and agree to abide by the organisation's standards. The organisation operates a technical helpline to assist consumers with queries about standards and will investigate any complaints about contractors approved. The NICEIC operates a certification scheme whereby any installation work may be tested and certified to meet appropriate standards. Registration is an important badge of competence for electricians.

Institute of Plumbing

A professional body registered as an educational charity. Its prime aim is the promotion of all aspects of plumbing engineering services in the public interest. Members of the Institute must be qualified (NVQ level 2 or equivalent), with at least 18 months' practical experience. All individual members must adhere to a five part Code of Professional Standards. In the event of dispute a Professional Standards Committee investigates and has the ultimate sanction of removing membership and entry on the Register of Plumbers.

Association of Plumbing and Heating Contractors

A trade association. Members are expected to comply with a code of practice and are 'vetted' by the association's field officers for qualifications and financial probity. There is a 'complaints service' to deal with disputes between members and customers

Heating and Ventilating Contractors' Association (HVCA):

This is a trade organisation mainly to assist contractors with legal and trade matters. Little indication of competence except that most members tend to be larger firms. An arbitration scheme and insurance backed guarantees are available.

Glass and Glazing Federation

Glass and Glazing Federation — Vetting of members includes a visit to their premises and financial checks. Members are expected to adhere to a 'code of ethical practice'. A free conciliation service is offered and this is run by the Chartered Institute of Arbitrators.

Deposits placed with GGF members are protected up to the lesser of £2,500 or 25% of the contract value.

Fair Trades

Members must have been in business for two years, have a clean legal history and a good financial rating. The previous customers of each member are contacted for references, which are maintained on an ongoing process throughout the membership. All relevant trades are able to issue an insurance backed guarantee – members are encouraged to provide these for free to their customers. Fair Trades also offer a conciliation service to consumers using one of their registered experts in case of dispute.

HomePro

HomePro — A service provided over the phone and on the internet at www.homepro.com. All contractors listed have been trading for at least one year, have had at least 10 previous customers selected at random from the contractor and contacted for references. All contractors are vetted for financial and legal credibility, and ongoing references are collected throughout the life of the membership to give an up-to-date picture of the performance of the contractor. All contractors are able to issue an insurance backed guarantee, and if disputes arise there is a conciliation service available. HomePro's directory can be found on Freeserve, BT Openworld, house.co.uk and through Britannia Building Society.

CITB **Construction Industry Training Board**

The CITB is an organisation to promote training in the construction industry (as the name suggests). The logo may mean that the company has a programme for training young operatives but it is not, in itself, an indication of competence.

Quality Mark

Not to be confused with the above, this is a government-backed scheme to provide a nationwide list of approved contractors and was the result of an aptly named "cowboy builders working group" at the DTI. The scheme will be rolled out over a four year period starting in 2002. It will require members to be suitably qualified, to meet quality standards and to offer an insurance backed guarantee to customers. The scheme aims to carry out annual inspections of contractors' work and will probably be run by an independent scheme operator. This scheme promises to be the most comprehensive quality accreditation but its success will depend upon how well it is operated and the range of contractors who are encouraged to join.

National Federation of Roofing Contractors

A trade association whose membership are expected to adhere to a code of practice and will have access to insurance backed guarantee schemes.

Quality Assurance

Quality Assurance accreditations are becoming quite popular, typically "BS 5750", "ISO 9001/2" often combined with the words "Quality Assured". These do not mean what they appear to. These schemes are about administration processes and reproducing consistent quality. They make no particular distinction between consistently good or consistently bad and only paperwork is inspected to maintain accreditation. The schemes are therefore no guarantee of the quality of site work.

Contact details for all the above are shown in Appendix 7, page 213, and most have websites listing current members. It is not enough to check for the logos, you must check that firms are actually current members.

Contractors join trade associations with the expectation of more business and trade related benefits. They are generally not difficult to join, because more members mean more fees. Inspection of contractors' work is costly and must be balanced with affordable joining fees, so in most cases site inspections are not carried out. Therefore, membership of trade bodies is no guarantee of site quality or competence. Some comfort for the customer may be gained through the various schemes for dealing with complaints and disputes, although the usefulness of these schemes is variable. Insurance backed guarantees, where available, are certainly worth considering, provided they are backed by a reputable and secure insurance company.

Membership of professional bodies requiring qualifications is a better guide to likely quality of work, although, even here, corporate membership does not mean that every operative will be qualified.

There will remain individual tradesmen who do not wish to join trade associations, through principle or cost, who will nevertheless provide excellent work at a competitive price. These contractors work almost entirely through recommendation and should not necessarily be discounted through lack of 'badges'.

'Quotation' vs. 'Estimate'

Traditionally, smaller builders usually give 'estimates' rather than quotations because with a wide range of building works from roof repairs to rising damp, accurate pricing is difficult until work has started and the extent of any defects can be seen.

Whereas a quotation is a fixed sum for a fixed amount of work (in legal terms, it is an offer, the acceptance of which forms a contract), an 'estimate' is the contractor's best guess at what the eventual cost of the job might be. Estimates cannot be compared like for like with other estimates because they are insufficiently definable and they leave the door open to abuse.

If you insist on a firm quotation, most contractors will add a safety factor to their price to cover the risk that the job may be more complicated than it seems, so you could be paying more unnecessarily. Where the extent of the work is not clear, ask the contractor to price a list of options.

For instance, water stains on the ceiling below a flat roof could indicate anything from a hole in the roof covering to the first signs of a completely rotten roof. Therefore, ask for prices for the following:

a)   Remove and replace roofing felt.
b)   As above plus renewal of timber decking (external ply or roofing grade chipboard).
c)   As above plus renewal of insulation.
d)   Complete new flat roof, plasterboard ceiling with plaster skim, including necessary protection.

Substantial repairs must be carried out in accordance with Building Regulations, which include requirements for adequate insulation (see Appendix 3).

This same list of options can be priced by several contractors. When the work is under way, inspect the area with the contractor to see how bad the damage is and agree the appropriate option. If it's roof work and if you don't like ladders, ask for damaged sections to be removed and shown to you.

For substantial works with a detailed brief or specification, insist on a quotation. The contractor can qualify his price, i.e. exclude certain items or limit his responsibility if he feels that he needs to safeguard himself against complications.

Invitations to contractors

If Planning permission or Building Control approval is required, obtain these before inviting contractors to price. (Many contractors will be reluctant to offer a price before the proposals receive approval and changes may be required that would affect the price.)

The checklist at the end of Chapter 6 indicated what information should be sent to the contractors for pricing. For smaller jobs all this may be condensed into a single letter.

As a guide, for internal alterations, new roofs, glazing, plumbing and small extensions, three or four prices would be appropriate. For larger extensions and loft conversions up to six quotes would be reasonable.

Specialist works

Restoration work can require a different approach, and the Yellow Pages is probably not the appropriate route to a contractor. Some contractors may simply affirm that they can do anything in any type of building. The question is not whether they can do it, but whether or not they can do it in an appropriately careful and sensitive manner and can be trusted not to use the 'unquantifiable' elements as a vehicle for overpricing 'extras'.

More than in any other case, recommendation, inspection of other work and detailed discussion with potential contractors are essential.

Pricing should be based on a 'schedule of rates' for specific items of work and labour rates and fixed profit on materials as a basis for unquantifiable items. Your overall budget should allow a substantial additional sum to cover the unexpected.

'Packaged works' – Double glazing, conservatories, fitted kitchens, bedrooms, central heating and bathrooms

Whilst building contractors are all competing for work, their work covers a wide range (from roofing, pointing, decorating to complete extensions), so building works cannot be 'packaged' in quite the same way as double glazing, fitted kitchens or central heating. Building firms are also quaintly old fashioned, by modern standards, in that they generally wait for the customer to make the contact if he wants work done.

The philosophy with some double glazing and fitted kitchen firms, however, is that "waiting for the punters to ring is no way to make money". Consequently some of these products are marketed much more aggressively. As these works are similar from one property to another (only the sizes are different), salesmen, usually on commission, rather than technicians, are often used to present the products to the customer.

Firms in this category generally advertise in the usual market place but with double glazing and fitted kitchens, telesales ("Hello I'm Tracy, and we at Acme Home Improvements have a great deal...") is a frequently used medium. Larger firms make and sell their own equipment. Smaller local firms may use wholesale suppliers whose names will generally be unknown to most consumers.

Both small and large firms may have high street show-rooms. DIY 'sheds' also sell these items and some offer a fitting service (so not exactly 'DIY' at all).

With double glazing, fitted furniture and conservatories, there are certainly variations in quality but double the price does not always mean double the quality. One assumed advantage of using a larger firm is that, having been around for some time, their guarantees may actually mean something and they have a 'reputation'. (Many consumers confuse 'reputation' with being 'well known', which is simply achieved through mass advertising.) Disputes with larger firms can be somewhat David and Goliath in nature because they retain top lawyers to deal with 'difficult customers' – and large firms are often no strangers to local Trading Standards officers. Central heating, being more functional than aesthetic, is not so much a showroom item and is still largely the province of local plumbing and heating firms although British Gas still seem to survive in this market. With plumbing and heating, all the equipment comes from plumbers' merchants so the same equipment is available to any contractor.

Use the same selection criteria outlined elsewhere to produce a list of contractors to offer a price. Actually getting a price from some firms can be difficult though.

THE 'PITCH'

Many of the firms in this sector, particularly in double glazing, do not like to have their prices compared with other firms, so their sales strategy is entirely geared up to obtaining a signed deal at the end of the 'presentation'. Some, even quite large, firms use a variety of arguably immoral tactics to achieve this. Typically: long pauses, to make it seem that you can't make a decision; banal questions to elicit agreement (a psychological ploy), like "Is this sort of good quality important to you?" and the telephone call to the manager, who is always available at 8-00pm, to obtain a 'special' discount. All nonsense and designed to bend your mind in the direction of a signed agreement.

THE 'CLOSE'

Invariably, after the chat and the survey you will be told the 'list' price and asked "How does that sound?" You will then be offered successive discounts based on how much the salesman perceives you to be losing your will to resist.

The 'close', in sales parlance, is something that clinches the deal: a special discount only available if you sign tonight or if you allow a signboard to be fitted outside. You will be told that you can sign now to get the 'special' discount but can cancel if you change your mind. But what's the point of signing until you are 100% sure? They rely on the fact that many people do not bother to cancel because a sense of commitment has been created by signing the deal.

There would appear to be only two ways to get the final discounted price from these firms. Method 1: Pretend that you are willing to place an order but keep insisting that the price is too high. When you have finally reached the salesman's bottom line (which could take quite some time) say, "Before I sign the order, I will need four references that I can check out", or: "I'll now need to check your terms and conditions with my solicitor". Then stand up and ask the salesman to leave. Be prepared for the sales-man to become quite unpleasant (although he might just be stunned!).

If you cannot face being this abrupt, use method 2: Tell the salesman at the outset that you will not be doing any deals now. You just want the lowest price he can give you on the basis that you may place an order in the future. With this method you are unlikely to get the discounted price, so when you have analysed other criteria, including references, contact the firms again and ask them for their lowest price if you go ahead now.

This makes it a bit like getting a price for an airline trip or buying futures on the stock market. Any price you are given is only valid if you buy now. You cannot ask "What will the price be if I buy in a month's time?" – they can't tell you.

I was recently told by a double glazing salesman that obtaining several quotations and making my own selection is "No way to do business". I immediately thought that he was better suited to doing deals on a street corner than in my sitting room but I told him, as politely as I could, that I'm the damn customer and I will choose how I do business. I noted that he then tried to salvage something from the interview by becoming more amenable. These characters are clearly trained to take advantage of people who appear to be 'soft targets', so the key is to remain assertive and not too friendly.

Chapter 8:

Selecting the Contractor – Analysing the Quotations and Placing the Order

There is a theory that suggests if all firms tender against the same specification, the lowest price must represent the best value for money. Whilst large, particularly governmental, organisations have accepted this for many years, those close to where the money is spent realise that the theory is flawed.

If a contractor has won a job because he has under priced some element, he will try to find ways of recovering his loss. Of even greater concern is the contractor who deliberately prices cheaply on the basis that he will make his profit on extra works. The skill lies in finding loopholes in the speci-fication, a similar skill to that of a tax lawyer I guess. With such a contractor, the final cost of the work frequently bears little relation to the tendered price. If you are only providing a 'brief' there is even greater latitude within which a con-tractor can price the work. Careful analysis of prices can sometimes reveal anomalies that need to be examined before a decision can be made.

Comparing offers

By way of example, a typical range of prices for a large single storey extension (2002 prices) may come in as follows:
  1. £30,500 2. £24,450 3. £24,200 4. £22,400 5. £15,000

These figures suggest that a reasonable price for the job would be around £22,000 to £25,000. Price 5 is very attractive and part of you will be thinking it's a bargain. The other part of you should be thinking that it's just too low for comfort.

The prices are much more easily analysed if they are broken down:

Breakdown	1	2	3	4	5
Footings floor & walls	16,300	13,400	13,800	12,300	8,100
Roof	8,200	6,500	6,800	6,200	4,200
Windows	3,000	2,600	1,600	2,300	1,800
Central heating	1,800	1,000	1,050	700	500
Decoration	1,200	950	950	900	400
Total	30,500	24,450	24,200	22,400	15,000

This breakdown shows much more of a story. No. 1 is higher on everything – probably due to higher margins and overheads. Price No. 5 is absurdly cheap so you would probably get either a cheap job or one with lots of 'extras'. Unless this firm came highly recommended, I would cross him off the list. Nos. 2 and 3 are comparable but No. 3 is curious. The price for the windows is very low. If you were to make enquiries and ascertained that the supply price of the windows was £1,000 trade, No. 3 may have forgotten to add his labour price to this.

Contractor No. 4 is lower than average on the structure and the heating but, if he is a bricklayer by trade and his brother is a heating fitter, it could explain such a saving. (Other firms may contract out both trades.) Going through the drawings or brief in detail with the contractor, depth of foundations, type of walls, sizing of roof timbers, specification of doors, coats of paint, etc. should reveal if the lower price is a result of shortcuts in quality or materials. If everything appears OK, there would seem to be only one point of concern – resources.

> To contact a contractor in order to query a low price, you need to be cautious in what you say. Do not indicate what the other prices are. Ask something like: "Your price for the roofing / heating, etc. is less than the average for this element. Would you like to check your price or can you explain why you might be able to do this cheaper than anyone else?" You must then make a judgment when you receive the answer. Any response that affects the price or offer must be confirmed in writing if you select that contractor.

A smaller contractor will have less labour available to juggle between jobs although a very small firm may complete one job at a time – so you will get their undivided attention. If resources are thin, however, labour problems due to sickness, offers of more lucrative work, holidays, deaths in the family, etc. are all likely to have a greater impact on your work.

Smaller firms may be less well resourced financially, so they may want a deposit to purchase the materials and this should be avoided. If you have a major dispute and find yourself at a financial loss, recovery of that money, from someone who has very little, might prove impossible.

In the above case, you might decide to rule out No. 4 on the grounds of lack of resources. Then you might get No. 3 to check his price. If he says that he has made a mistake but will honour his price, you could consider it a bargain. Alternatively, you may prefer to go for No. 2, on the basis that for an extra £300 you will not start the work with a contractor who is already looking for ways of recouping £1,000 of lost profit by scrimping on materials or looking for 'extras'.

PC AND PROVISIONAL SUMS

If the cost of a particular item of work or equipment cannot be accurately priced at the time of quotation, the contractor may include within his offer a 'Provisional Sum' or 'PC (Prime Cost) Sum'. This is an estimate of the amount he thinks the item will cost but it is not a firm price. You will be expected to pay the actual cost once it is known. Check quotations for these provisional sums and, if different contractors allow different figures, disregard them for the purposes of comparing prices. Be wary if some contractors include an element of work within their price and others show a PC sum for the item. In this case, in order to compare like with like, you may need to take the matter up with the firms to ensure that they all price the same way for the same thing.

COMPARING SCHEDULES OF RATES AND MATERIALS SPECIFICATIONS

If you have asked the contractor to provide 'rates' for specific items of work or even a list of labour rates and a 'materials uplift' (percentage profit on the cost of materials), check that the rates quoted by your preferred contractor are not substantially higher than the norm. A low overall price but high labour and material rates is frequently an indication of a contractor who relies on extra work to make his profit. Items on a schedule of rates may be negotiable.

If the contractors have provided details of construction methods against your questionnaire (see Chapter 6, page 64), compare the offers. You may need to do some research to make suitable comparisons. (See Resources in Appendix 7, page 216.)

INTUITION

Talk to a contractor as much as possible whilst he is viewing the job – just to see what kind of person he is. We may not be perfect judges of each other but if one of your invited contractors just makes you feel uneasy – if there is something about his attitude that disturbs you – do not ignore it.

This may not be very useful where packaged works are sold by a salesman. He will not be the person that you end up dealing with and, in any case, his personality may be a carefully crafted veneer.

There are also some more obvious pointers. If a contractor calls to survey your property and he arrives in a 10-year-old rusting heap, what does this say about the way he runs his business? Are you sure that he'll take more care over your roof than he does of his van? If a contractor walks into your house with muddy boots or plaster-covered overalls, how careful will he be about site cleanliness?

EXCLUSIONS

Read through any exclusions carefully. Some may be confirmation of things that you have agreed with the contractor, but any surprises should be queried. If one contractor has excluded something that another contractor has allowed for, check how it affects the respective prices.

COSTS AND INFLATION

Projects in excess of 12 months' duration often include formulae for increasing the quoted price to cover inflation. With domestic work this should not be necessary so check that the price is 'fixed' for the duration of the work.

Terms and conditions

If the contractors accept your contract clauses or your proposed 'standard' contract there is nothing to compare in this regard. Some contractors may include their own terms or suggest an alternative form of contract. Carefully read their submission and see how it affects your protection in the event that things go sour. The clauses that I have included in Appendix 1, or versions thereof, provide you with protection in several essential areas.

If the offer comes with its own pre-printed order form it

will usually also have the firm's own terms and conditions
on the reverse. You **must** read these. Ask for anything that
you do not understand to be clarified. If timing is important to you and specific times are quoted on the offer, make
sure there isn't a clause saying 'time is not of the essence'
because this will negate any quoted time. Contracts with
this clause should be avoided in any case – although they
cannot take away your rights under consumer legislation,
they may complicate disputes about delays.

Some smaller firms who are 'uncomfortable with legal
matters' may refuse to accept written conditions. Provided
your proposed conditions are in 'plain English', contractors
should have nothing to fear if they are honourable. You may
wish to point this out and ask which clauses they have a
problem with.

UNFAIR TERMS

Check that the contractors' terms are not unduly weighted
in their favour, e.g. if there is nothing about their progress
but stiff penalties for delays in payment. Check that they do
not appear to absolve the contractor of something that
should remain his responsibility. For example, if they seek
to limit damages for delay or faulty work or materials.

Certain terms may be declared unfair by the courts and
cannot be enforced. Examples would include clauses that:

* Allow the contractor unfairly to increase the price of
  the contract.
* Forbid you to withhold money for outstanding or
  defective works.
* Prevent you from withdrawing from a contract while
  allowing the contractor to do so.
* Exempt the contractor from any liability in the event
  of damage to your property.
* Prevent you from taking legal action.
* Exclude liability for death or injury

If you find a clause in a contract that is clearly unfair you may wish to take it as an indication of the contractor's general attitude and take your custom elsewhere.

TERMS VS TERMS

Where both parties to an agreement use their own terms, the final assertion of terms prior to the contract being formed will generally determine which prevails. (The 'last shot wins' rule.) Nevertheless, it is safer either to get the contractor to use your terms, to accept the contractor's terms (with agreed modification if necessary) or to reject the contractor's offer.

Guarantees

Defects in some building works can take several years to appear so with double glazing, a new roof or an extension, a five- or ten-year guarantee is of more comfort than a one-year guarantee. With standard contracts for larger work, e.g. JCT Minor Works, six-year warranties are typical.

With heating, plumbing and electrical works most defects are likely to show within 12 months, so long term guarantees are less common and of less benefit. Any guarantee is only as good as the firm offering it: if a small contracting firm has been around for less than five years, statistically, the chances of it lasting long enough to honour a ten-year guarantee are not favourable. For any substantial work, obtain an insurance backed guarantee. There may be an additional charge for this.

Specialist materials or treatments such as roof coverings and rot treatments may have their own extended guarantees, and these are usually given by the firm that produces the material rather than the contractor. The material must be installed or applied strictly in accordance with the supplier's instructions. Make sure the contractor complies with this or ask if the manufacturers would be prepared to inspect the installation to ensure that it complies with their warranty.

References

Always obtain references. This applies equally whether you have selected the firm from an advert, from a recommendation, or a high street shop. Written references are of no use because, if the contractor is a crook, they will be written by himself and the referees will be his relatives. Ask contractors to provide you with a list of customers for whom they have recently carried out similar works and from which you can pick two or three random references.

Most people are happy to help with such enquiries. Ask detailed questions about the work to make sure they are genuine. If all the referees sound the same and give little detail beyond just saying the firm is great, they are probably set up. Having established that referees are genuine, ask their appraisal of the contractor in terms of:

Reliability and continuity	–	Turning up when agreed and not leaving the job for days unfinished.
Cleanliness and protection	–	Use of dustsheets, clearing of rubbish, etc., care of furniture and fixtures. Protection against weather.
Attitude to queries	–	How helpful and responsive to quality queries.
Quality of work	–	Attention to detail, especially with finishes.
Attitude to additional works	–	Fair or unfair claims for and pricing of extra work.
Keeping to programme	–	Did the work start and finish on time?

For substantial work, where referees sound friendly, ask if

you can visit the property to check for yourself the standard of quality.

If you get any negative comments, make a judgment about how this affects your proposed work. If any contractor fails to provide or appears particularly cautious about providing references, it could be because he has trouble remembering a customer whom he has not upset. I would strike any such contractor off my list.

If a contractor boasts that he does work for the local authority, this does not mean much. Councils employ both good and bad contractors.

Comparing 'design and build' proposals

The difficulty here is that the 'design' will vary in each case so there is no simple 'like for like' comparison and each contractor's proposal cannot be judged solely on the final price. The receipt of a variety of design solutions and prices will require a more careful analysis. Your best means of comparison will be to check previous work: if referees sound friendly when you speak with them on the telephone, ask if you can pay them a short visit to see the completed job.

Final checks

TRADE AND PROFESSIONAL ORGANISATIONS

If your preferred contractor's advertisement or headed notepaper shows any of the logos listed in Chapter 7 (pages 71 – 76), and if you haven't done so already, check that the firm is a current member and that there are no adverse reports about them. You may need to 'read between the lines' of any cautious sounding response to your enquiry. If the contractor displays a logo that I have not listed and there is an inference that it is some sort of badge of competence, check out both the organisation and the contractor. Contractors have been known to invent impressive sounding organisations, so watch out!

INSURANCE

The contractor must have adequate 'public liability' insurance cover. Most bona fide contractors will carry a minimum of £1,000,000 insurance. Asking the contractor to provide a copy of his current insurance certificate is a reasonable request before the work starts. Any designer or design and build contractor must also have design liability insurance. You can take out joint insurance with the contractor to increase the level of cover if required.

FINANCE

Before you enter into a contract make sure that your funds are in place or will be in place when you need to pay the contractor.

Most quotations will show VAT as a separate item. If there is no mention of VAT it is best to query it. It could be that the firm is not registered for VAT, but this would have to be a very small firm (turnover below £54,000 in 2001-2).

Contractors' quotations are usually firm for a certain period – 1-3 months maybe. If you have taken some time deliberating over your decision, check that the chosen quotation is still valid. You may also wish to check the contractor's availability.

Placing the order

The acceptance of an offer (by the person to whom the offer is made) forms a contract in law. It is therefore your last opportunity to make sure that you are getting what you want and that all relevant details are agreed. Any change from now on could cost you more money. If you are using a pre-printed contract document ensure that both signatures are in place before the work starts. If you are relying on a 'bond' to cover loss if the contractor goes bust, verify with the insurance provider that cover is in place once the contract has been initiated.

DEPOSITS

Try to avoid paying a deposit. A high proportion of consumer complaints in this sector are a result of 'grab a deposit and run' bogus contractors. Any general building contractor who does not have the cash to finance at least two to four weeks' work should be avoided. An agreement to pay an early valuation covering materials delivered to date would be preferable to a deposit in advance, because you do at least own the materials. Many glazing and fitted furniture firms insist on a deposit to cover expensive materials that need to be specially ordered or made to measure. Ask what protection is offered in the event that the firm goes bust. Paying a deposit by credit card should provide protection against fraud through 'joint liability' legislation; check with your card issuer, but pay no more than 25%.

STAGED PAYMENTS

Monthly payments are the norm for contracts lasting longer than four weeks. Alternatively, specific payments may be made on completion of sections of the work. Agree the payment regime with the contractor before placing the order and include the details with the contract documents (see Chapter 11, page 120).

LETTER OF ACCEPTANCE

Unless the contractor has a pre-printed order form, or you are using a formal contract with a pre-printed legal 'Agreement', you should complete the deal by writing to the selected contractor accepting his offer. This letter is a 'contract document' (i.e. the letter itself forms part of the contract) and should include:

- A list of the documents, drawings, etc., that you have provided for the contractor to price and a reference to the contractor's offer.

- Any verbal agreements made, work included or excluded, etc.
- The start date or period within which the work should start and the length of the contract period or the completion date.
- The agreed payment regime (if not covered elsewhere).
- A requirement for the contractor to acknowledge receipt of your letter.

A sample letter of acceptance is shown in Appendix 6.

The contractor may want additional copies of drawings and the specification (page 62), so you should expect to provide these.

PRE-PRINTED AGREEMENTS AND ORDER FORMS

If you sign a contractor's order form, maybe with an accompanying schedule or sketch, ensure that the paperwork includes everything that you have agreed and that you have a copy of every sheet. It is common for special details to be discussed and agreed with a salesman (the standard of making good or some special item of additional work for instance), only to find that the workmen carrying out the work have no such instructions. Remember: if it's not on the paperwork, it's not part of the contract. If there is no room, put a big asterisk on the form and write against it "To be read in conjunction with my separate letter of this date". Then write a list of any pertinent points that you have agreed, keep one copy and give the other to the salesman, or send it with the order.

BUYING ON CREDIT

It is mostly 'packaged' works where a credit arrangement will be offered as part of the deal, because the offer of finance is a useful selling tool, and can also be quite a lucrative sideline for the company. There are numerous sources of credit from bank overdrafts through re-mortgages to loan companies. If you intend to borrow money for the work, research your options and understand that if finance is offered by the contractor, he is providing two quotations: one for the work and one for the credit. You may be better off getting the finance elsewhere.

Buying on credit is really outside the scope of this book, and is only ancillary to this discussion but the following should be noted:

1) Beware of low prices and a heavily sold finance deal. It indicates a firm more interested in finance deals than contracting.
2) The approved method of showing interest rates for comparison is the APR (Annual Percentage Rate), but comparing how much you will actually pay over the term (e.g. £150 per month x 36 months is £5,400. £130 per month for 48 months is £6,240) is also fairly straightforward.
3) Check whether interest rates quoted are fixed or variable.
4) Check the penalty clauses for paying the loan off early.
5) When entering a credit agreement, make a note of the company supplying the finance. You may need to make contact with them separately.

Under the 1974 Consumer Credit Act, if you conclude a credit agreement

a) after verbal face to face discussions have taken place with the salesman and
b) the agreement is signed away from the seller's premises, e.g. at your home,

you should receive a confirmation of the agreement within seven days. You have up to the date you receive the confirmation plus a further five days in which to cancel the agreement. Cancellation must be in writing and is valid from the date of positing, so proof of posting is advisable (a

Recorded Delivery receipt would suffice). Ordinarily, where a credit agreement is cancelled, the 'linked transaction', i.e. the contract for the works, will automatically be cancelled as well, but do check that this is the case (if you should later dismiss the contractor or he goes bust, the reverse will not apply).

CANCELLATION – OTHER THAN WITH CREDIT AGREEMENTS

You may decide that you no longer wish to go through with a purchase, e.g. if you succumb to the pressures of a double glazing salesman and sign a form to get rid of him. Provided the salesman's visit resulted from an unsolicited call to you, e.g. you were 'telephone canvassed', you have a right to cancel the agreement within seven days under the Consumer Protection (Cancellation of contracts concluded away from business premises) Regulations 1987. Firms are actually required (under a 1998 amendment to the Act) to advise customers of this right of cancellation. If this is not done the agreement may be considered void in any case. Again, written notice within the seven day period is required for cancellation without penalty.

If you have approached a contractor and subsequently entered into a contract with him you have no right to cancel without penalty. This does not automatically mean that there will be a penalty, it simply means that the contractor may be able to claim damages against you to recover any expenses, although he must provide reasonable proof of his costs.

Chapter 9:

Overseeing the Works

Attitude

Cordial formality is the appropriate approach to contractors. If you become too friendly, it will be difficult to maintain authority. If you appear arrogant and treat building workers as a lower form of life, they may find a construction equivalent of peeing in your soup. As indicated in the introduction, mutual respect is the desired relationship.

There is a world of difference between taking an interest in what the contractor is doing and constantly leaning over a tradesman's shoulder, so aim to know what's going on without being a nuisance.

Many contractors play a constant game of musical chairs with their resources. This is not necessarily their choice; it is the nature of the work. Workloads will vary, unforeseen work will take time to complete and even with the most efficient planning system available, inevitably two contracts will require a plasterer at the same time, and it will be the day the plasterer is at a funeral. In addition to this, merchants do not always deliver when they say they will and sometimes deliver the wrong materials. Contracting can be like juggling with balls that constantly change shape and size, and sometimes multiply into three!

The 'that's not my problem' attitude will be unhelpful. It is the contractor's job to manage these variables but it is quite unrealistic to expect him to get it right every time. In return for a generally diligent attitude to progress and a respect for your wishes and your budget, a contractor should be allowed a little flexibility.

Pre-commencement matters

On larger contracts, it is worth discussing the work in detail one more time with the contractor before he starts work. Cover the following:

Start date; completion date; storage of materials; welfare facilities; health & safety issues; arrangements for dealing with changes to the work (written instructions); the necessity for meetings throughout the works (useful on larger contracts).

Go through the specification or brief to ensure that the contractor is clear about any elements that are complex or which may be open to the contractor's interpretation. If there is a designer involved, a meeting with all parties will be useful.

On work taking longer than one week, ask for an indication of how long each major task will take. On projects lasting for more than two to three weeks, ask for a detailed programme so that you can monitor the progress of the work (Fig. 7a shows a simple 'milestone' programme, whereas Fig. 7b, on page 100, is a bar chart for a more complex project). As a 'lay' project manager, without a programme showing when each task is to take place, you will not know if works are on schedule (see 'Progress', on page 101). Few small contractors are good at issuing programmes, nevertheless you should insist that you are given some kind of plan of action.

CLEANLINESS AND PROTECTION

Most people are unfamiliar with the amount of mess and dust that can be created during building work. The whole household must be prepared for this.

Nevertheless, a careful contractor can minimise the problem. Dustsheets should be used where contractors are working in occupied areas and on all access routes, but it is impossible to stop dust falling on shelves and small surfaces. Therefore, remove any ornaments and expect to dust the

14 Acacia Road new conservatory

Programme of works:

Start date / delivery of materials	Mon 16th Aug
Strip off roof of existing sun room	Wed 18th
Erect screen to protect dining room	Thu 19th
Demolish walls	Fri 20th
Complete new walls	Wed 25th
Complete new glazing bars	Sat 28th
Complete glazing	Wed 2nd Sept
Flooring	Fri 4th
New radiator, finish electrics, etc.	Mon 7th
Completion date	Wed 9th

Fig 7a A simple 'Milestone' programme

whole place thoroughly once the contractor has finished. You may need to clean kitchen surfaces daily. Cutting chases in walls or cutting though walls to form new openings will be quicker with power tools but these devices reduce masonry to dust – lots of it. Using a bolster and chisel or cutting from the outside will create less dust but takes more time. Discuss these matters with the contractor and ask him what steps he can take to minimise the problem.

New equipment and materials must be adequately protected from the weather and from damage. Driveways, pathways and anything likely to be damaged during the work should be protected. The same goes for any existing fitments or equipment that you are providing for the contractor to fit, e.g. a fridge/freezer for a new kitchen. It is useful to take photographs of all surrounding areas and items for use, before the work starts, as evidence of prior condition.

Ensure that the contractor keeps shared driveways and

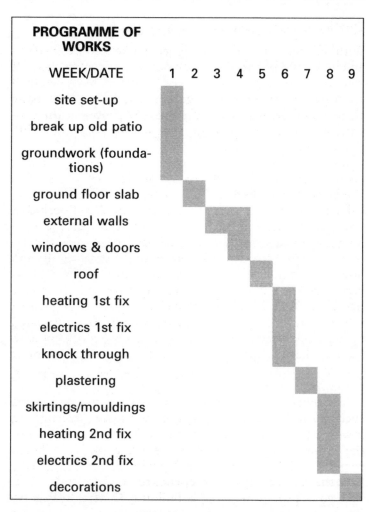

Fig 7b A bar chart programme for a more complex project

'common parts' of flats free from mess and adequately protected. 'Reasonable precautions' on your part may include temporarily moving garden plants that are at risk and keeping your car away from the skip.

Quality and progress

With substantial work, a designer is likely to be involved and he should be asked to do an occasional quality check. If you are entirely on your own, use the notes in Appendix 3 on page 164 to provide a general check on some basic elements of the work and, if you know people in the construction industry, ask them to have a look around before too much progress is made.

When the contractor starts work, check how careful he is about cleanliness and tidiness. As previously mentioned, a site littered with tools and old materials is a bad sign: you will need to monitor quality here very carefully. Check that waterproof membranes are continuous and that there are no gaps in insulation and thermal barriers (see Appendix 3 on page 165). Check overall 'setting out', i.e. that walls and doorways, etc., are positioned as shown on any drawing (it is best to do these checks in the evening, when the contractor has left: a client walking around checking everything with a tape measure and a copy of the drawing is not appreciated by most tradesmen). If you see anything that does not look right or that looks botched, query it with the contractor. If you think that you are being fobbed off, get a second opinion.

If the work involves specialist or less common elements, such as lead or zinc roofing, marble or granite cladding, etc., it would be worth researching this so that you are aware of the requirements: contractors are more likely to botch something that they are unfamiliar with and do not actually have the correct skills or experience to do properly.

If your project requires a Building Control officer to inspect the works, be as friendly as you can, offer him a cup of tea and ask what he thinks of the rest of the work, for example, the things that he is not necessarily required to check.

It is important that you are satisfied with the general level of workmanship before you part with any money. It could cost you much more to have poor workmanship put right

later. If the job only lasts for a day or two, take some time
off work so that you can spot problems before too much
progress is made.

MAINTAINING AN EYE FOR DETAIL

The things that frequently result in the client not getting
what he had in mind are the details that are seen every day.
Discussing the minute details of how high the electrical
sockets should be from the floor may seem tedious but
frequently you don't know how important these things are
until you notice that they just don't look right.

Some of us have more of an eye for detail than others. If
you have a partner with this particular talent, put him or
her in charge of visual inspection. Check that all verticals
and horizontals are true (use a spirit level if necessary but
again, not in front of the tradesman unless you want to
make a point!).

SUBCONTRACTORS

Contractually, management and co-ordination of subcontractors are the responsibility of the 'Main Contractor' but
this duty is often not their strong point. If a subcontractor
does not have any specific instructions about how things
should look, he will do things the way *he* thinks they look
best or the way that is easier. Tell the main contractor that
you want to be introduced to each subcontractor before he
starts work and go through his work in detail to highlight
any special requirements. You can also advise the 'subby' of
any house rules that the main contractor may have failed to
pass on. Do not instruct a subcontractor to carry out additional work. If a subcontractor indicates that something you
want will be 'an extra', ask the main contractor to provide
you with a price for that work. If you think that the work
should have been included within the original price, insist
that the work is carried out at no extra cost. (It will be for the
main contractor to argue with the subcontractor about why

it was missed.) Direct arrangements with a subcontractor will be outside the contract and can lead to arguments about responsibility and cost. They are best avoided.

DECORATORS

If decorating is to form part of the works you will want a finish that is better than you can do yourself, otherwise you might as well do it yourself. Ensure that sufficient drying out time has been allowed and that the work is carried out by an actual 'decorator'. Few general tradesmen have the patience and perfectionist qualities that are required to produce a good result with decorating. The key to a good finish is in the preparation. Surfaces should be rubbed down to a smooth finish (before the first coat and then between coats) and paint or varnishes applied after all the dust has settled. Gloss paint on bare timber will require, typically, two coats of primer (one will probably show bare timber after rubbing down) one or two undercoats and one or two top coats. Varnishing should be a laminate made up of two to four thin coats. Any decorator that takes only one day to decorate a sizeable room is more suited to 'toshing out' offices than high class domestic work. The following are strictly unacceptable: runs in paintwork; patchy, tacky varnishing; bubbles, stretches, gaps or overlaps (except at corners) in paper hanging.

SITE SAFETY

Building sites can be dangerous places; there are many accidents and several fatalities each year in the construction industry. Given also the aphorism "most accidents happen in the home" this should make domestic construction work a lethal combination. Suffice to say that ladders, tools, electrical leads, holes in the ground, combined with children, pets and even adults unfamiliar with the dangers, provide a concoction that requires some vigilance.

Where children are concerned, physical barriers for very small children and a full explanation of the dangers to those over 4 years would be better than "Don't go out there" which is clearly an invitation to a curious child.

240 volt power tools are prohibited on building sites. If the work in your home is more than a simple maintenance job, the contractor should use 110-volt power tools with a transformer. Loose tools and materials should be kept safely out of harm's way and secured somewhere at the end of each working day.

Scaffolding is potentially the most dangerous 'plant' item and where this is used you should inspect it regularly to ensure that it complies with safety standards. See Appendix 3 on page 193.

If your work includes any demolition, there are special safety rules about this. Take advice from a professional.

PROGRESS

Compare progress regularly with the contractor's programme of works. The odd day or two where no contractor is on site may be unavoidable, but where no work is carried out for several days, or promises of a return to work do not materialise, this is bound to affect the programme and you should insist that progress is restored. If you remain unsatisfied, treat the matter as a dispute. See Chapter 12 – 'Prolonged delays', on page 131.

Of course, delays due to inclement weather cannot be blamed on the contractor and the agreed period in which the work should be completed may need to be extended, see page 119.

Paperwork

With most small-scale domestic work, correspondence during the course of a project is unnecessary, but certain written matter can prove invaluable if trouble should develop later on.

RECORDING PROGRESS

Memories are notoriously unreliable and it's easy to lose track of time, so using a diary to record key dates throughout the period of the works will build a suitable picture of progress:

Mon 10th Jan   Contractor starts on site

Tues 11th   No labour on site – weather fine. Sand, cement and aggregate delivered AM

Wed 12th   No labour on site – weather fine

Thurs 13th   No labour on site – showers late PM

Fri 14th   Contractor on site PM

In three weeks' time when the work is running a week late, if the contractor says he could not work during the first week because of bad weather or lack of materials, you won't have to rack your brains to decide whether this was true.

It is important to record weather conditions where there is external work. Note also when each section of work is complete so that it can be checked against the programme. (Taking weekly photographs with a date camera could also prove useful.)

CONFIRMATION OF INSTRUCTIONS

This may seem laborious for simple matters but then all matters seem simple until they become complicated:

Client: "Why are you painting that wall pink? It's supposed to be blue."

Contractor: "No mate, it says pink in your specification."

"I know, but we changed it."

"I don't remember that."

"But I told your colleague Fred."

"Ah, well Fred's working on another job this week."

Etc.

If writing letters is not routine for you, confirming each

instruction may sound like a bind. On large construction projects when it is necessary to give an on the spot instruction, a pre-printed form is used. This arrangement is ideally adapted to domestic work: just purchase a duplicate book from a stationer and jot down any agreed changes – give the top copy to the contractor. If even this seems a little over the top for a small job, take a sheet of A4 paper and find a folder, clipboard or something substantial to pin it to. Write down on this sheet every change that you agree giving date and details. Do this in front of the contractor and leave the folder in a prominent place. This will provide an open record of all changes agreed. Fig. 8 shows an example record sheet.

Verbal instructions/Changes agreed	
26/May	Render finish agreed to side walls only of extension.
29/May	Depth of bedroom cupboards reduced to 600mm to allow for bedroom door swing.
31/May	Two additional single elec. sockets requested for bedside table lamps.

Fig 8 Record sheet showing agreed variations

Before issuing any instructions to vary the work, you must establish whether this will affect the price. See Chapter 10, page 117.

If a contractor is unable to obtain an item or cannot do something the way he expected, he may suggest an alternative and advise that this will involve extra cost (he would be in breach of contract if he varied the contract without authority). The contractor is obliged to meet his obligations at the quoted figure and the increased cost of the alternative is his risk in providing a quotation. (The exception may be where something was genuinely not foreseeable when the job was priced.) If you write a note 'accepting' the changes, this may be taken as accepting the additional cost as well. The wording of your reply is therefore critical. It should read "In respect of your letter (or *advice*, if verbal) of . . . date, I have no objection to the proposed change." This confers no acceptance of the additional cost and, if your note is not queried by the contractor, the boot is entirely on the other foot at final account time because there has been no suggestion that the additional cost will be met by you.

ARCHITECT AS AGENT

If you employ an architect and use a JCT Minor Works contract, the architect will be your 'agent' in dealing with the contractor and only he should issue instructions. With less formal contracts you should agree with the architect which of you will issue instructions to the contractor and the other party should refrain from so doing in order to avoid confusion. In either case, instructions should be agreed between you before they are issued.

MAKING A NOTE OF OTHER DISCUSSIONS AND AGREEMENTS

The larger the project, the greater the likelihood of matters arising that will require discussion and agreement. The outcomes of some of these discussions may not appear at the time to warrant written confirmation but, if there is an outcome of any sort or any kind of agreement, make a note of it.

On large projects where there is much co-ordination of trades, an architect involved, or if progress needs to be regularly analysed, you should arrange periodic formal meetings and these should be minuted.

> On my first big project as a trainee there was a site foreman called George Saunders, a quiet and amiable man. George kept a site log in which he noted everything: who visited site and when, when materials

were delivered, the weather and just about everything that anyone said. You would be amazed how many times queries and minor disputes were settled by reference to George's log.

KEEPING DRAWINGS UP TO DATE

On large projects there can be several drawings and everyone, including the subcontractors, needs to be working to the same latest version. Traditionally, when drawings are amended a suffix letter is added to the drawing number and the alteration noted somewhere on the drawing, i.e. "Rev. B relocate washing machine". It is then a case of ensuring that everyone is using Drawing No. 1234/B for example, rather than 1234/A. A written instruction should be issued to accompany any revised drawings.

Dealing with problems

If difficulties occur, timely and appropriate action can frequently prevent major disagreements or disruption to the work. Generally, construction problems may be divided into two categories: a) practical difficulties, e.g. unforeseen construction obstacles, and b) dissatisfaction with the contractor.

PRACTICAL PROBLEMS

Practical issues alone are frequently the easiest to deal with. If the issue is the result of error or oversight, this needs to be taken into account at some point but it is frequently unhelpful to start with who is to blame.

1. *Identify and define the scope of the problem.*
    For example, the bath will not fit, because the space between the two end walls is 20mm too short. There is no other place for the bath. The tiler is due tomorrow.

2.   *Identify ways of overcoming the problem and consider possibilities against the parameters of time, cost and quality. Think about repercussions.*
     For example, use a shorter bath/cut back the plaster on the walls/demolish and rebuild the end wall.
     Remember that the contractor probably has a lot of experience and can probably suggest a few solutions. Discuss the matter with your partner or a friend if another opinion would be useful.

3.   *Agree the solution and confirm agreement in writing.*
     This allows work to proceed. (Your selected solution may be dependent upon your confidence about who has to pay for it.) For example, cut back plaster and chase the wall at the bottom end of bath only – this will not affect the tap holes. (Pay particular attention to ensure that the bath is not forced into position and damaged.) Delay tiler for two days. Make a note of extra costs.

4.   *Define responsibility.*
     Is it clear from the specification or brief who was responsible for avoiding the problem or was there insufficient detail? Could the problem have been foreseen with a proper survey? Should the contractor have noticed this detail or was he simply working to drawings by someone else? Is the problem due to poor sequence of working or poor planning? It is easy to become angry at the situation but better to step back and take an objective view (as would be taken by any third party whom you might pay to intervene).
     Many small problems where responsibility is difficult to apportion can be settled amicably on a 50/50 basis or examined at final payment stage when a little 'give and take' may be applied. Where the cost is substantial and you cannot agree with the contractor about the solution or who is responsible, you may need to involve a third party to adjudicate (see Chapter 12, page 130).

DISSATISFACTION WITH THE CONTRACTOR

If you are concerned or unhappy about some element of the work, be it quality or progress, speak straightaway to your main contact for the work (e.g. the supervisor), rather than a tradesman or subcontractor.

If you are not satisfied with the response, or promises do not materialise, you should immediately write to the contractor advising, formally, of your concern. A reasonably friendly letter frequently does the trick (keep copies of all correspondence).

It is most important that this is not ignored, just because writing a letter is too much trouble. Something along the lines of sample letter 4a in Appendix 6 (page 207) would be appropriate in most such cases.

There is a fine line between dissatisfaction and a dispute, but if a contractor does not provide a swift and acceptable response to your first query, go into 'dispute mode', so that the contractor is left in no doubt about your position. If you receive an inadequate response from the contractor on a technical matter you will need to involve a third party. Try the sources listed in Chapter 12, on page 134.

Financial control

The finances of a routine domestic improvement contract are not particularly complex. Just keep a running account of the works so that you can see your liability at a glance. Start with the accepted contractor's price and add to this any additional works as they are agreed. Use an estimated figure for any extra work if you don't have a firm price. Record each payment made as well.

It is very easy to keep these simple records on a single sheet of paper but if you've been itching to find a use for that computer spreadsheet software – now's your chance! Chapter 11, Payments (page 128), shows how a full record of the contract can be kept on spreadsheet format.

To keep a simple running account, something like Fig. 9 would suffice:

Cost of works		
		Cumulative
Agreed price	£12,000	£12,000
Additional works:		
Extra electrical work	£300	£12,300
New guttering	£1,300	£13,600
Extra radiator (estimate)	£150	£13,750

Payments made		
		Cumulative
1/04 Deposit	£500	£500
25/04 Interim payment:	£6,000 (less deposit) £5,500	£6,000
16/05 Interim payment	£5,000	£11,000

Fig 9 Running account for a medium sized contract

At the end of the project, once the final payment is made, the cumulative cost of the works should add up to the total cumulative payments – see Chapter 11, page 125.

Chapter 10:

Variations

Why a contract may be 'varied'

The perfect contract will be fully specified in advance, will hit no difficulties and require no changes during its performance. Such contracts are rare. Difficulties with conveying what the client had in his mind's eye, omissions by the designer and the complexities of the construction process, can all result in a need to 'vary' the work from that originally agreed with the contractor. Understandably, variations are the most common reason for disputes, or surprise, when the final bill is received.

There are, broadly, four situations that may arise which would require a variation to the contract.

1. Requests by the client for additional work.
2. Suggestions of extra or alternative work by the contractor.
3. Unforeseen circumstances.
4. Items not adequately specified.

(Of course, there is the possibility that none of these will apply and the contractor will be just 'trying it on'. The following should help identify these cases as well.)

1. REQUESTS BY THE CLIENT FOR ADDITIONAL WORK

Clients frequently ask the contractor to carry out extra work without due consideration to cost: "Could you just . . .

mend that broken shower; paint that extra wall; fit a dado rail; tile the other bathroom?" etc. Most contractors will testify to the fact that about 40 per cent of their work comes from the 'can you justs'. It is easy to underestimate or lose track of these extras and they can be an open cheque for a contractor to add, excessively, to his profit or offset losses made elsewhere.

Always obtain a rough estimate of the cost of any additional work before it is carried out, or agree with the contractor how the work will be priced. Make a note of exactly how long the extra work takes and what materials are involved. For any substantial extra work, you must obtain an accurate price in advance.

2. SUGGESTIONS OF EXTRA OR ALTERNATIVE WORK BY THE CONTRACTOR

Even the most trustworthy contractors seem to have a skill for selling extra work that an insurance salesman would envy: "How about having an extra roof light over the stairs?"; "The plasterwork in here is awful, why don't I just hack off and re-plaster the whole room? It's no problem!"

Extras are rarely a problem – for the contractor. The contractor is very likely to think of something that you did not, after all, he's probably seen it all before and he may have some very good ideas. The key is not to assume, because the suggestion is made in such a friendly way, that you won't be charged for it. You might wish to ask why he didn't make the suggestion when he was pricing the job, but you must always ask "How much will it cost?"

3. UNFORESEEN CIRCUMSTANCES

A contractor may ask for more money if he discovers something that was not foreseeable when he priced the job. Minor complications are part of his risk in giving a quotation so you will need to decide if the claim is reasonable. Let's look at two examples:

a)   A contractor forming a new doorway stumbles across electrical wiring running horizontally around the room from a switch to a wall light. He advises that he will need to get his electrician to re-run it in a new position. This would probably involve new chases and making good. It could be quite expensive.

b)   A contractor is installing new heating. The client has stated that he does not want to see any horizontal pipe work (traditionally, where there are suspended (timber) floors, the pipes are run below the floorboards). The contractor finds that in the extension part of the sitting room there is a solid (concrete) floor and says he didn't realise this, the floor was carpeted the same as the rest of the sitting room and he checked the timber part. He suggests two alternatives: Running pipework around the skirting, which will be visible, or forming a pipe duct in the concrete floor but at an additional cost.

Much of English civil law is based on the concept of what is 'reasonable'. Yet when it comes to a dispute in law, only a court or an arbitrator can decide what is reasonable. This is the reason why the construction industry keeps so many lawyers employed. The following would be my own adjudication of the above cases.

a)   In most buildings, the wiring for the lighting runs above the ceiling and down to light switches. The wiring for power (electrical socket outlets) runs below the floor. It is not unreasonable for a builder to assume that this is the case. He could have run a wiring detector instrument across the wall before providing a price but this would not be normal practice in this situation. If the client wanted the door in the position specified, the wire would have to be moved in any case and he would have to pay for it. It is also unlikely that other contractors tendering would have noticed this peculiarity. I would consider this genuinely unforeseen and agree that this is extra work.

b) The fact that the contractor did not notice that the extension had a solid floor is an oversight on his part. Solid floor extensions are actually very common but, regardless of this, the contractor should have checked the floor in each area where the pipework was to run, particularly if the client had stated that surface pipework was unacceptable. The contractor should create a floor duct for the pipes at his own expense.

    This is the sort of thing that is frequently missed by salesmen with limited practical knowledge. The client should not pay for their mistakes.

Some difficulties are more a matter of negotiation and not entirely clear-cut. Being unduly harsh on a contractor who stumbles across something unexpected may not be the best way to encourage him to give you his best work. If you have chosen the cheapest price, it is likely that the contractor will not want to absorb too many difficulties. If you pay a 'decent' price, the contractor should not claim for extras every time he hits a snag. If the item is substantial and you cannot agree, treat the matter as a dispute. See Chapter 12, page 130.

4. ITEMS NOT ADEQUATELY SPECIFIED

This is a common problem with domestic work. If there are holes in the specification or your brief, they may need to be dealt with as the work proceeds. Asking the contractor to allow for "everything that will be required in order to produce a workable finished job" gives you some protection, or at least a point to argue from, if you miss something obvious. If the contractor fits a cheap bevel edged skirting where you envisaged an intricate moulding the question is – what did you ask for? If you forgot to specify the details, you should not be surprised at the result. If the contractor fails to fit any skirting though, this would not be a complete and finished job.

If an architect has failed to specify something and yet that thing is clearly required, then it would need to have been paid for anyway. If omission by an architect causes abortive work or unnecessary extra costs you should view this in the context of the whole service provided. If you incur substantial costs through negligence, you should seek recompense through a reduction in fees or a claim for 'damages'.

Issuing instructions to the contractor to 'vary' the works

'INSTRUCTIONS' DEFINED

It is customary, in most projects, for the client (or his agent) to issue 'instructions' to cover changes or confirmation of items not precisely detailed (some written contracts specifically confer this right on the client). If the contractor advises that there will be no increase in price due to the change, write "at no extra cost" on the instruction. You can examine the issue later to determine if there should be any reduction. If the contractor advises that the change will involve additional costs, make a note of the estimate but *not on the instruction*. The instruction is simply to allow the work to proceed as required; it is not an agreement to meet any specific extra costs. You should reserve the right to verify or negotiate any additional costs and agree the final figures at the 'final account' stage. This avoids you having to accept a price under duress – e.g. to avoid delaying the work. If, however, you believe that a price given for additional work is exorbitant, it may be better to query it there and then, rather than deferring the argument until the work is done.

Where work is carried out after you have signed a contractor's 'order form' the arrangements may be different and if you request any variance to the work, you may be required to complete a 'variation order'. In this case, you will be committed to whatever additional price is quoted.

Some variations may reduce the cost of the works. The traditional way of showing changes in a running account is to omit the cost of the original work and add back the cost of the new work. For example:

Omit: four wall lights in sitting room   (£200.00)*

Add: single pendant in centre of room   £75.00

* brackets indicate a minus figure

Pricing extra works

Whereas the original contractor's price could be compared with competitive offers, prices for additional works cannot. You need to ensure, as far as possible, that no higher profit margin is put on extra work. This is done by using the original priced quotation as a guide to the pricing of extras. There are three ways to do this:

1. MEASUREMENT

If unit rates are included in the quotation, e.g. £x per square metre for walling, plastering, flooring, etc., £x per metre length for fencing, piping, wiring guttering, etc., you can use these rates to price extra work.

If rates were not quoted, ask the contractor to price the extra work on a unit rate basis and then check with a trade organisation or another contractor's rates to see if the rate is fair.

Where quotations are based on a 'bill of quantities' (where the total price is made up of rates and estimated quantities of work) it is expected that any additional work should be priced on the same rates. With priced work you cannot usually insist that rates for additional work are derived on a pro rata basis from the lump sum price but it is a good basis for negotiation or as an indication of what is 'fair and reasonable'.

2. LABOUR AND MATERIALS

"Day work", as hourly labour rates are known, is frequently used when it is difficult to determine the amount of work that will be involved. Verify labour rates with trade associations and prices of materials with merchants. (A reasonable 'margin' for the contractor would be 10-20 per cent on his trade price.) The problem with day work is that there is no incentive for the contractor to finish the work quickly, so unless you feel that the contractor is totally honest and diligent, it can be an open cheque. All jobs involve these two elements so lump sum prices can be broken down and verified in this way.

3. COMPARISON

If additional work is just more of the same type, rather than something quite different, use the quoted price as a guide. The more detailed the contractor's breakdown, the easier this is. For example, if four new radiators were priced at £400, the price for one additional radiator should be around £100 unless the additional work is more complicated. Similarly, if a price of £300 was given for 65 sq. metres of plastering, then 300 ÷ 65 = £4.61 per sq. metre. Any additional plastering should be comparably priced.

Using this method for valuing additions to smaller jobs may overvalue them if the original price included hire of scaffolding, travelling time, etc. If the additional work does not increase the contractor's overheads, a slightly lower rate might be more fair.

If you do not believe that a price for additional works is fair, you may decide not to include the works in this contract but to obtain competitive prices and have the work done later. If this is not practical you could issue an instruction and expect to argue the matter at final account stage.

Changes to the 'contract period'

The length of the contract is rarely critical with domestic work and if there are no penalty clauses there is little you can do if it runs over a bit. The concern is that it should not run over substantially. Being a little formal about the contract period, even for smaller jobs, keeps the contractor focused on time.

If additional work is requested or the contractor advises that the work will take longer to complete for a reason you deem acceptable, make a note of it – together with the estimated extra time. If the contract is larger and more formal, confirm this with an 'instruction'.

An extension to the length of the contract could involve the contractor in extra costs, e.g. if he is hiring a container. If your extension of the contract is a concession on your part, make it clear that the extension of time will be "at no extra cost".

Chapter 11:

Payments

Interim payments

For projects lasting longer than four weeks, the contractor may want 'interim' or staged payments and this should be agreed at the outset. This chapter deals with how to go about this.

THE TWO CARDINAL RULES

Rule 1: For small jobs pay only on completion. Otherwise, pay for no more than the value of the work and material that has been supplied to your satisfaction. If, due to the contractor's poor performance you want to terminate the contract or if he goes bust half way through the work, getting back any overpayment may be difficult – in the latter case, even impossible.

There is a further, less severe but frustrating problem with overpayment, and that is the removal of incentive for timely completion of the job. Given the previously mentioned contracting game of juggling resources, it is natural for a contractor who is under-resourced both financially and in terms of labour, to put most of his effort into the jobs where there is most money to be had. This can become a problem particularly towards the end of a project where the money outstanding is small.

Rule 2: Pay contractors and professionals promptly. People may not necessarily stop working if you do not pay them on time, but they will not give of their best. More serious is the fact that failure to pay is a breach of contract. In this situation, your contractor would be at liberty to 'renegotiate' his price.

HOW MUCH TO PAY

The simplest arrangement, where the work can be divided into clear 'stages', is to make payments as each major element of the work is completed, e.g. £2,000 on completion of foundation, £3,000 on completion of walls, etc. Where banks and building societies are involved in the finance for works, they prefer this arrangement because it is easy to check. The amounts paid should be based on the quotation breakdown. The danger is that the early stages will be over-valued – but this can be checked by comparison with other quotations.

Wait until the relevant section of the work really looks complete and the contractor moves on to the next section before you pay.

The traditional method is to make a payment based on the value of the work completed on a particular date (usually once each month).

Valuing the works

Whether the contractor submits his own version of what he considers to be complete so far or simply asks for "some money on account", you should carry out your own valuation to make sure that you are not paying over the odds.

Take the quoted figure for each part of the work (from the contractor's tender breakdown) and multiply this by the percentage that you feel has been completed to give the present value (as shown in Fig. 10 on page 124, a representation of a typical interim valuation). Use the contractor's programme of works and visual inspection to determine this. Add to the totals any extra work for which a price has been agreed. This may be all or partially complete and is calculated in the same way. If prices for additional work have not been checked and agreed you could include a notional (conservative) sum or, if the sums are fairly insubstantial, ignore them until the final account.

Valuing the work cannot be an exact science, particularly for the householder managing his own works. So arguing over £100 for an interim valuation on a contract worth £5,000 is simply not worth the effort.

If progress towards the end of the contract starts to slow down and only a small amount of work is being completed each week, write to the contractor to record the delay and refuse to make further interim payments before the final payment. In any case, always withhold sufficient money from any penultimate payment to ensure that the final payment is substantial; thus providing a suitable incentive for completion. This is particularly important if you haven't included a 'penalty clause' in the contract.

UNFIXED MATERIALS

You are not obliged to do so unless it is specifically required in the contract, but it is accepted protocol that the cost of 'unfixed' materials and equipment (e.g. bricks before they are built into a wall or a radiator before it is hung on a wall) are included in any valuation. However, if you include these costs, don't go paying £100 for four bags of cement! Ask to see the merchant's invoices to verify any material costs, and expect to pay only for major items or bulk supplies where just one or two invoices cover the amount; you should not be expected to check a dozen invoices for small items. Pay only the cost price of the materials: the contractor's profit is only payable as part of the completed work. Once you have paid for materials, they are yours. Ensure that the contractor does not take them away for use on another job.

Do not be concerned that if you pay for materials on one

valuation when they are loose and subsequently pay for the work when completed (which of course includes those materials) you will be paying twice. This possibility is avoided by deducting any previous payments from each valuation (as shown in Fig. 10).

VALUE ADDED TAX

VAT is payable on all home improvement works, provided that the contractor is VAT registered (some insulation works and heating controls attract a lower rate of VAT).

If a contractor sends a client an interim account based on a staged payment, i.e. the amount is a predetermined sum, VAT should be shown. If payments are based on 'valuation' where a contractor has sent you an "Application for payment", it should not show VAT. If you disagree with the amount and/or produce your own valuation, the amount of VAT should be calculated on the figure that you agree is due. For example:

You agree, or advise the contractor, that you are prepared to pay £5,200 on this valuation. The payment should be calculated thus:

Works to date as agreed	£5,200.00
VAT @ 17.5%	£910.00
Amount due	£6,110.00

Some contractors incorrectly send VAT invoices instead of applications (and then have difficulty reconciling their VAT records because the amount they receive is less than their invoice). The invoice (which is the official VAT record) should only be issued once the valuation has been agreed. This is particularly relevant if you intend to reclaim the VAT because the work you are having done is for business purposes, e.g. if you are self-employed and you are having an office built in your garden.

VALUATION No 2			
	Quoted price	% complete	value as at (date)
Footings floor & walls	13,050	100%	13,050
Roof	6,800	50%	3,400
Windows	2,300	90%	2,070
Central heating	900	20%	180
Decoration	950	0%	0
Contract work total	2,400		18,700
Additional works agreed:			
Electrical work	1,500	20%	300
Revised brickwork specification	200	100%	200
Total additional work			500
Total value of work completed to date			19,200
Allowance for materials on site:			
Roof tiles			400
Central heating boiler and equipment			350
TOTAL THIS VALUATION			19,950
Less amount paid in previous valuation/s (No. 1)			
* or as a deposit excluding VAT			(12,300)
			7,650
** Less 5% retention *(if agreed)*			(383)
AMOUNT DUE			£ 7,267
plus VAT			

*   **If you have paid the contractor a deposit it should be deducted from the first interim payment.**
** **Retentions are discussed in Chapter 13, page 148.**

Fig 10 A typical interim valuation

CASH PAYMENTS

If you intend to pay any amount in cash, pay only the boss or the supervisor, ask him to count it in front of you and *get a signed receipt.*

FINAL PAYMENTS

When the work is complete, or possibly a little before this, the contractor will submit his bill. In unmanaged contracts, this is frequently the time when the client suffers a sharp chest pain or needs to move urgently to the smallest room in the house! Having digested the advice in this book, hopefully, you will be saved from this unpleasantness.

Check the contractor's account with your own running account of the project and analyse any prices for additional work to satisfy yourself that they are fair. You do not have to agree with the contractor's first figures for elements of the work that were not priced in advance. Check the final prices of any elements of the work that were included within the quotation as 'Provisional' or 'PC' Sums (see Chapter 8, page 85). The final price of these items may be more or less than the provisional sum. Ask for suppliers' invoices where appropriate and check percentage profit or labour charges in order to verify the final cost is fair – just as you would for a variation. If you have any queries, submit these in a letter to the contractor together with your own calculations.

The 'balance sheet' format of producing a 'final account', as Fig. 11 on page 128, is usually adopted because it is easy to check that the contract sum plus adjustments on one side equals all the payments that have been made, or are now due, on the other.

Remember to include any work that has been omitted as well as anything that has been added, together with the appropriate options where alternative methods or amounts of work were proposed.

Agreeing a final account

I have indicated elsewhere that final accounts are frequently a negotiating matter. I do not mean by this that agreeing a value for additional works should be like the negotiation that takes place when selling a used car. Endeavour to agree the **correct** price for any additional work, calculated as explained in Chapter 10, albeit that there may be elements of 'give and take' on some issues where the brief was not entirely clear or where some difficulty could have been avoided if the contractor was a bit more resourceful.

Practical completion

'Practical completion' is the point at which the client has full use of the building, although there may be minor items outstanding. The time between the agreed completion date (agreed in the contract or correspondence forming the contract) and the practical completion date will be the period of overrun and the duration of inconvenience or incurred costs. It is an important date to note if you intend to make a claim against the contractor. Evidence would be required as to the scale of inconvenience (beyond that reasonably expected given the work involved) and you would need to establish actual financial loss, e.g. reasonable restaurant bills for each extra day that your kitchen could not be used.

SNAGGING

Snags, in building speak, are items that require remedial work or finishing off, rather than difficulties (for which the industry has more colourful terms). When the contractor announces that everything is complete, carry out a close inspection of the entire work, making a list (a 'snagging list') of any items that require attention. For example, paintwork that needs touching up, mastic missing from joints, filling that has shrunk and needs refilling, poor grouting, etc., and hand this to the contractor, keeping a dated copy for yourself.

Unless you intend to hold a retention (see Chapter 13, page 148) despite agreeing a final account figure, do not make the final payment until all the snagging items are complete. There is no incentive for the contractor to return to complete small items if all the money has been paid. If the work has required Building Control approval, obtain a 'Final Certificate' from the Building Control officer, before you release the final payment.

If you have arranged for an insurance-backed guarantee, verify that this is in place before you make final payment. An inspection of the work may be required by the guarantor.

In the event that you pay the contractor his final payment and then discover something is not completed, it is not a case for despair. You will not have thrown away any rights, you may just have made getting the work finished a little more difficult.

	contract price	valuation No. 1 % complete	value
Ground work	4,000	100	4,000
Walls windows etc	5,300	75	3,975
roof	2,400	10	240
heating	650		0
electrics	740		0
decorations	1,120		0
external work	780	50	390
Contract price/value to date	14,990		8,605
Variations			
1. Add base for shed	100		100
2. Change to bricks	250	estimated	300
3. Change to radiators	120		
4. Change to wallpaper	(40)		
net variations	430		400
CONTRACT TOTAL	15,420		9,005
value to date less already paid excluding VAT		deposit	(500)
			8,505
less 5% retention			(425)
NET PAYMENTS	**deposit**	**500**	**8,080**
VAT at 17.5%			1,414
Cheque required.			9,494
TOTAL NET PAYMENTS			

Fig 11 Accounting record showing initial agreed price, variations, staged payments and final account. The cumulative payments shown as 'total net payments' should equal (or 'balance') the Contract total

| valuation No. 2 | | Final account £ | |
% complete	value		
100	4,000	4,000	
100	5,300	5,300	
100	2,400	2,400	
20	130	650	
30	222	740	
	0	1,120	
80	624	780	
	12,676	14,990	
	100	100	
agreed	250	250	
		120	
		(40)	
	250	430	
	13,026	15,420	
			cumulative
	(8,080)	(13,279)	
	4,946	2,141	
	(247)		
	4,699	**2,141**	15,420
	822	375	
	5,521	2,516	
			15,420

Fig 11 (cont'd)

Chapter 12:

Disputes

If you find yourself in a dispute with your contractor, despite the precautions outlined elsewhere, you should strive to resolve the matter as quickly as possible, because poor memories or bad feeling can complicate any issue.

The more complex the project, the greater the scope for problems, but most disagreements with a contractor will fall into four categories:

- Failure to perform, i.e. excessive delays.
- Poor quality of workmanship.
- Disagreements about the specification or the extent of the work.
- Charges for additional work.

It is unwise and unnecessary to spoil a relationship for the sake of minor irritations. Equally though, you should not put up with broken promises, shoddy work or profiteering. Dissatisfaction with the contractor should therefore be accompanied by an appropriately measured response.

If you find yourself in a dispute with a contractor that you have been unable to resolve amicably, there are three possible courses of action:

- Mediation or arbitration – this is the use of a third party, usually with some expertise in the field in question. A mediator will attempt to get both parties to agree to a solution. An arbitrator will listen to both sides and make a judgment.

- Enforcement of the contract – any contract may be pursued under the law. Legal advice will need to be sought as to the merits of your case.
- Enforcement of consumer legislation – there are a number of Acts of Parliament designed to protect consumers from unfair treatment in commercial transactions and satisfaction may be obtained through the courts if the contractor breaks the law.

It is frequently the case that awareness of these courses of action and preparedness to use them – particularly if communicated to the contractor – are sufficient to resolve the matter. Much of how to proceed will depend on the nature of the dispute.

Causes of disputes

PROLONGED DELAYS

This is not usually a 'dispute' in the ordinary sense of the word because in most cases the contractor cannot deny that there has been a delay if the work is behind programme. With performance related delays (i.e. lack of action by the contractor), it is more a matter of the client deciding that enough is enough.

If you use a written contract, it will probably include a clause that requires 'diligent progress of the works' (or similar wording). The first recourse in this situation is through the contract: if there is no improvement three to four days after your initial letter, write to the contractor advising him that his lack of action is in breach of contract and that the breach should be 'remedied'. (This means that he should do what is necessary to comply with the contract.) You should quote the appropriate contract clause. It may not be necessary for the contractor to remove all labour from site for a delay to constitute lack of appropriate performance under the contract. So you can pursue this action even if the contractor turns up periodically just to give the impression that he is progressing the work.

If you receive no reply or see no substantial action within a further 7 days you may wish to consider terminating the contract. How far you go with this may depend on: how concerned you are about the delay, how much you have paid the contractor and whether you could get the work completed by someone else for the money you have yet to pay. Ultimately, there can come a point where the hassle of throwing the contractor off the job is less than the misery of putting up with a half completed job.

In the case where there is either no written contract, or a contract that has no reference to progress, the implied terms provided by consumer legislation are relevant here: The 1982 Supply of Goods and Services Act requires that work is performed "within a reasonable time". Unfortunately, the wording of the act suggests that you need to wait for the work to be well past the agreed completion date, rather than just progressing too slowly, before you can do anything. Nevertheless, a warning shot to the contractor (in the form of a letter, please!) citing this legislation may do the trick. See 'Routes to satisfaction' on page 134.

DELAYS CAUSING EXPENSE TO THE CLIENT

A delay in completing the work may cause you additional expense. For example, if you need to stay in a hotel, or if your granny cannot take possession of her annexe and needs to stay on in her rented accommodation. Recourse, in these cases, would be to seek damages for breach of contract. It should be noted though that any award of damages may be limited to obvious expenses. If the contractor is not aware of your granny's present accommodation circumstances and any contingent expenses, he is unlikely to be liable for such costs. If you have included a 'penalty clause' in your contract you may have a right to enforce this. (See Chapter 13, page 149.)

POOR WORKMANSHIP AND NON-COMPLIANCE WITH THE SPECIFICATION

Most good contractors will know if some element of their workmanship is not up to the appropriate standard and will need little encouragement to rectify it. If the contractor is uncooperative, the first and most obvious line is "I'm not paying for that!" As indicated in Chapter 10, page 116, in most cases (unless you have signed the contractor's own order form) you can instruct the contractor to do or alter something without agreeing to pay any more and to leave negotiations until the end of the contract. Make thorough notes about the disagreement including any additional labour hours and materials and take photographs if appropriate. If a contractor refuses to rectify the problem or denies that there is anything wrong, it will generally require third party involvement to sort the matter out. If there is a professional involved, he should be the arbiter of quality.

If there is no professional involved but you know someone in the construction industry, ask him if he would give you his opinion. The contractor may not welcome someone outside the contract inspecting his work but, if the observations are sound, he may be persuaded that a more official arbiter might reach the same conclusions. If you speak to another tradesman about the problem, bear in mind that some tradesmen love nothing better than 'slagging off' their competitors. One of these clever Dicks is of no use to you! Any third party must be seen to be objective and impartial. If this route is inappropriate or unsuccessful, see 'Routes to satisfaction', overleaf.

OVER-CHARGING

If you believe that charges for extra work cannot be justified, either because you think the work should have been included in the original price or because the price does not equate with the original – competitive – pricing of the work, you could either negotiate or refuse to pay any more than you think is appropriate. If the contractor firmly holds his position, and intends to take legal action to obtain payment, a third party resolution will be required if you still dispute the contractor's claim. You must act quickly to avoid incurring unnecessary legal costs or claims for interest on late payment.

Routes to satisfaction

If discussion with the contractor is unproductive, you should seek advice without delay. Below is a list of sources of third party arbitration.

❏ Trade/professional organisations

If the contractor is a member of a trade or professional organisation, contact the organisation and ask if it has any mediation or arbitration scheme. Check out: a) the cost; b) the time taken to deal with a problem; c) whether it will just send letters or, in the case of a quality issue, someone to inspect the work; d) whether you are bound by the decision of any intermediary. Some of these schemes are very ponderous and legal action may be more effective and cheaper where appropriate.

❏ Consumer advice centres

Contact a local consumer advice agency (see box opposite) and see which course of action they recommend.

❏ Professional intermediary

For quality and charging issues it may be necessary, in order to pursue action in law, to have a professional third party inspect the work and produce a report to support your action. Use the RIBA, RICS, CIBSE, I.Struct.E., etc., (details in Appendix 7, page 213) to find a suitable 'expert'. You will need to pay for this, but don't let this delay your action. You may be able to recover the costs from the contractor if a court finds in your favour. These organisations may also be able to suggest a suitable mediator if appropriate.

❑ ARBITRATION

If your contract includes a clause requiring disputes to be settled by arbitration, try to work with the contractor and contact the organisation specified in the contract or call the Institute of Arbitrators to find a suitable person. There is an arbitration scheme operated by the Royal Institute of Chartered Surveyors and the Royal Institute if British Architects. This scheme can have disputes resolved within 21 days but both parties must agree to be bound by the findings of the adjudicator.

❑ A SOLICITOR

If you are advised by your consumer advice agency that a solicitor is required, find a solicitor who is familiar with consumer building contract cases. Local 'Law Centres' provide initial free advice and in some areas these are very helpful. Your consumer advice office will have contact details.

❑ LEGAL ACTION

Any of the above sources of advice may recommend or lead you to taking legal action. Where you believe a contractor is in breach of contract, this may be a less expensive route than arbitration – but take advice. I have outlined the process later in this chapter.

Consumer Advice

Most local authorities have a department providing advice for the consumer and these offices act as a

> local branch of the Office of Fair Trading. The names
> for these departments vary; e.g. Consumer Advice
> Bureau, Consumer Affairs Department or local Trad-
> ing Standards Office. Use any of these names and
> the switchboard at your Town Hall should direct your
> call appropriately.
>
> The work carried out by these agencies varies
> across the country. Some may only deal with cases
> where the contractor has contravened consumer
> legislation but others may try to help you with any
> kind of dispute.
>
> Citizens Advice Bureaux are manned largely by
> trained volunteers. They may help with general advice
> or writing letters but will have less clout than TSOs
> where consumer legislation is concerned.
>
> A useful publication in the UK is the **Community
> Services Directory**. Copies are held by the above
> agencies and at libraries. The directory will detail the
> services provided by organisations in your locality so
> you can contact those who are most likely to be of
> help. The directory is also available on a website –
> www.justask.org.uk

MULTIPLE ADVICE

Advice agencies become very irritated by what they call
'advice shoppers': consumers who are apt to contact several
agencies and get them all to fight their case. In addition to
being a waste of limited resources, different approaches by
agencies may conflict and errant contractors can play one
against another. Find an adviser who sounds helpful and
interested in pursuing your case and stick with him.

Disputes with 'packaged works'

With some double glazing and fitted furniture packages,
the company makes the materials themselves so you cannot

easily get another contractor to slip in and finish off the job. Large deposits can also be a disincentive to termination. So what can you do in this situation?

If you receive no satisfaction from the supervisor, write to the firm's Managing Director – by name. (Letters addressed to 'the Managing Director' are usually either junk mail or complaints, so they are frequently intercepted by a secretary and passed down to a lower level. See Sample Letter 7.) If the problem is about quality, ask for a senior official of the company to inspect the work. In the meantime, invite a suitable knowledgeable third party to attend at the same time in order to support you.

If you believe that the firm's actions (or lack of) are contrary to consumer legislation, contact the local consumer advice office.

If the work cannot be completed by others due to the use of specialist materials, it may be necessary to terminate the contract and ask the company to remove their partially completed conservatory/kitchen/windows from site (within 14 days or you will employ someone to dismantle and dispose of it). You may then need to sue them for the disruption and expense caused and the return of any money paid.

Clearly all this would be a last resort but it can be done if you can demonstrate that you have exhausted all other avenues. In most cases letting the managing director of the firm know you are prepared for this will be all that is needed.

Unlike other packaged works, with central heating or plumbing, the work could, if it came to it, be completed by another local heating or plumbing firm. So treat this type of work as any other.

PAYMENTS WHEN IN DISPUTE

Never pay more than the value of the work that has actually been completed to your satisfaction – but act 'reasonably': e.g. if you are unhappy with just the tiling in a new bathroom withhold payment for the whole of the tiling but not for the whole works. Withhold enough to cover the cost of any defective works plus reasonable 'damages' for getting another contractor to finish off or correct the defective work. If you withhold payment unreasonably, a contractor may put his resources elsewhere and if you complain that he is not diligently progressing the contract, he could claim that you are in breach of the contract for non-payment. This is an unpleasant spiral and one to be avoided at all costs.

CREDIT AGREEMENTS

Generally, if the work is being carried out through a credit agreement arranged by the contractor, you will not be expected to pay anything until you have signed a form to say that you are happy with the work. Do not sign until the work is 100% complete.

If you discover a problem after you have signed a satisfaction note, write to the contractor about it and send a copy to the credit company. Continue any credit payments, unless the lender advises you that you can stop: withholding payments to the credit company could affect your credit rating. Pursue the matter with the contractor and, if the problem is serious, seek legal advice regarding your rights under the credit agreement.

Under the 1974 Consumer Credit Act (section 75) the firm granting the finance may be equally liable with the supplier/contractor if there has been any breach of contract or misrepresentation. You may need to establish that there has in fact been a breach of contract (i.e. a defect may be evidence that the work has not been carried out with 'reasonable care and skill' as required by 'Sale of Goods and Services' legislation) before you can use this provision.

Terminating the contract

Termination is the contractual equivalent of a nuclear warhead. It is far better used as a deterrent than as a weapon because its use can result in a whole load of other problems.

Nevertheless, termination can turn out to be the least stressful course of action if you are faced with a really poor contractor.

You will only have a right to terminate the contract if the contractor has committed a serious breach, i.e. he has done or failed to do something that is fundamental to the agreement between you.

The following circumstances may warrant termination due to breach of contract:

- Failure to start.
  That is failure by the contractor to commence work or deliver any materials for a considerable time after the agreed commencement date. In the case of equipment manufactured in advance, factory delays may affect delivery and the company's own terms may indicate that delivery times cannot be guaranteed. It must be quite clear that the contractor is not just late but appears to show little likelihood of commencing the work within a reasonable time, for instance if he cannot give a date or has missed two or three dates already.

- Poor quality of work.
  If it becomes clear that either all or a major part of the work is of exceptionally poor quality, it would be reasonable to insist that the work is put right before any further work is carried out. If, after following the procedures outlined above, the contractor fails to make any reasonable attempt to resolve the matter, termination of the contract would be reasonable.

- Lack of progress.
  If progress stops or slows to the extent that the period for the contract would be substantially extended and the contractor fails to improve productivity despite your requests, it may be reasonable to terminate the contract. (Delay must not be due to weather, genuine

problems with materials or other issues that are beyond the contractor's control. In the case of double glazing, etc., where the company both manufactures and installs, it cannot claim that manufacture or delivery problems are outside its control.)

- Other breach of contract.
  If a contractor contravenes a specific crucial obligation in your contract, or an obligation that may be implicit in any contract for work in someone's home, you may be justified in terminating the contract. Liquidation/ bankruptcy of the contractor would qualify. Serious abuse of hospitality or aggressive or indecent behaviour might not actually prevent the work from continuing but in severe cases termination might be justifiable.

Remember, if you act unreasonably, the contractor could defend any action and make a claim against you for loss of profit. However, if you do feel that termination is your only recourse, seek advice and support for your decision from the local consumer advice office, Citizens Advice Bureau or a solicitor. If you are working with an architect, seek his advice through this procedure.

Bear in mind with this course of action that the work will need to be completed by another contractor and this will involve you in further work and possibly expense that you may not be able to recover.

NOTIFICATION

To terminate the contract after giving a written warning (see Sample Letter 6, page 209), you should send a recorded delivery letter to the contractor's registered office (or principal place of business), advising that you are terminating the contract. State the reason (e.g. failure to perform, despite previous complaints) and the basis on which you are taking the action (e.g. breach of contract). See Sample Letter 8, page 211.

AFTER TERMINATION

Offer the contractor a reasonable period – say 14 days – to collect any equipment belonging to him and any materials that have not been paid for. Give further warnings, by registered post, before you dispose of anything that the contractor may lay claim to. Put any materials that you have paid for somewhere well away from anything that the contractor is required to remove. (A good reason for being very specific about which materials you are paying for in any interim payment!)

Example		
Works carried out:		
Foundations	100%	£2,000
Ground floor slab	100%	£1,000
Walling	25%	£1,000
Bricks left on site		£ 600
Total value of works completed and materials left at date of termination of contract.		£4,600
Less:		
Cost of Surveyor to value works		£ 200
Cost of remedial works as detailed in attached quotations		£ 700
Cost of disposal of rubbish		£ 100
Total deductions		£1,000
Net value of contract		£3,600
Less amount paid to date		£3,000
Amount owed		£ 600

Fig 12 A final account at termination

Make an accurate assessment of the value of the works carried out. You may need a quantity surveyor to help you with this.

If another contractor is required to complete the works, ensure that any remedial work is priced separately, and obtain alternative quotations to ensure fairness. Then draw up a final account showing the value of the works carried out to date (see Fig. 12).

You need not make final payment to the dismissed contractor until the works have been completed and you know the full extent of any remedial works.

If the bottom line of the account is a minus figure; that is, if you have paid the contractor more than the amount owed, getting the money back is unlikely to be a simple matter. You may need to take legal action to recover your loss.

GETTING THE WORK FINISHED AFTER TERMINATION

Invite prices from other contractors to complete the works and talk through the job in detail with each contractor, making careful notes about what is required to complete the work. Discuss the usefulness of any materials left on site and any remedial work required. Ask them to consider taking over the subcontractors if you are happy with these. Ask for a price broken down as follows:

1.   Work required to rectify or replace
     existing work. Detailed separately.   £ . . . .

2.   Contingency sum to be used in the
     event of unforeseen problems with
     existing work.   £ . . . .

3.   Work required, as specification, to
     complete the job.   £ . . . .

     (Break the items down as your original brief where
     appropriate.)

Items 1 and 2 can be deducted from any monies owed to the first contractor.

The contingency sum need not be spent unless you agree that something is truly unforeseen.

Finishing off items of work where safety or potential damage is an issue will involve risk. It is in your own interests to ensure that any subsequent contractor takes great care and has the appropriate attitude: a contractor who is sympathetic to your plight will be better than one who is resentful of 'tidying up someone else's mess'.

Where the dispute has been about quality and there are structural elements to the work, engage a structural engineer to verify that the work carried out is sound.

SUBCONTRACT WORK AT TERMINATION

Subcontract work is automatically terminated upon termination of the main contract and the subcontractors are left to pursue any outstanding claims for money with the main contractor. Disputes between main contractor and subcontractor, whilst not your problem (contractually), will still have an impact on your work. It may be wise to tread very carefully when dealing with interim payments at a time when you are considering the possibility of terminating the contract.

If it can be established without doubt that monies you have paid to the main contractor in respect of subcontract works have not been passed on to the subcontractors, you should seek legal advice about deducting the appropriate sums from the main contractor's final account.

If, despite your best efforts, the main contractor retains monies due to the subcontractors, the subcontractors must understand that you will not pay for the same work twice.

Once you have terminated your contract with the main contractor you are at liberty to make whatever arrangement you wish with any other trades. If subcontracted work is nearly complete, you may wish to enter into direct contracts with some subcontractors but ensure that your new builder is happy with this arrangement. You will need to keep a close eye on co-ordination.

The following action will be required:

a)   Obtain firm prices from the subcontractors for the completion of the work or ask them to negotiate with your new main contractor.

b)   Assess the fairness of the subcontractors' prices (compare them with elements in the main contractor's tender).

c)   If entering into a contract with subcontractors, remember price, quality, scope of work and time should all be clearly stated. An exchange of letters should suffice for this rather than another formal contract. Include within the letter the date from which the new contract will run.

d)   If the new builder is taking over the subcontract works, ensure that he takes full responsibility for their work.

Contractor going into liquidation

If a main contractor is having financial difficulties, his subcontractors will usually be the first to suffer, so in the event of subcontractors failing to turn up or complete work, you should try to find out if this is an early warning of trouble ahead.

If a main contractor goes bust he may be considered in breach of contract. Subcontractors may be owed money even if you have paid the main contractor. They should not expect you to meet their losses and have no right to claim back any equipment that has been fitted. They must look to the main contractor's administrator or liquidator for payment. If there are loose materials on site, subcontractors may have a claim on them despite the fact that you have paid for them. This involves matters of 'title of goods' and will require legal advice. Neither the main contractor nor the subcontractors will have any right to enter your property after termination. Any unauthorised entry will be trespass.

If a main contractor goes bust on a substantial project, it would be advisable to 'close the site' immediately and engage a quantity surveyor to carry out an inventory of the works and deal with the other parties. This may be paid for out of anything that you still owe the main contractor.

Were the client's obligations fulfilled?

Rights and obligations are applicable on both sides of any contract and whether or not the following points are spelt out in any contract documents, they may, in most cases, be taken as implied terms in any domestic building contract.

The client must:

- Allow free access to the site as necessitated by the contractor's work programme.
- Provide any facilities to enable the contractor to work on the site (including welfare facilities if agreed).
- Give any necessary directions or instructions in good time to avoid disruption to the works.
- Deal with, obtain approval from and pay fees where required, to meet local authority requirements (where this is not being dealt with by the contractor or designer).
- Provide any 'free issue' equipment or materials (purchased by the client for installation by the contractor) in good time.
- Pay the contractor at the appointed time/s amounts commensurate with the work carried out.

If you do not meet these obligations, you will weaken your position in the event of any dispute and the contractor may have grounds for claiming breach of contract and seeking compensation for any loss.

Taking legal action

RECOVERING LOSS (DAMAGES)

If you have suffered loss, the road to recovery is via the law – but it can be a long road. You can take action to recover the return of money owed to you (e.g. payment you have made in advance for goods not supplied), for losses incurred as a result of action by a contractor (e.g. damage to your property), or for the necessity to engage a further contractor to correct faulty work or costs incurred as a result of the contractor's previous breach of contract. Claims for compensation can also be made for loss of amenity, inconvenience and/or anxiety caused by the dispute. Before taking any legal action though, you should do two things. Firstly, try to make sure that the contractor is capable of paying any amount claimed. A permanent place of business and evidence that the contractor is still trading should be verified (there is no point in taking legal action against someone who cannot be found or who has no money). Secondly, discuss the matter with a solicitor or your local Trading Standards Office to get an opinion as to whether or not the case is worth pursuing. Many solicitors offer a reduced-fee first consultation for such enquiries.

If your local Trading Standards officers believe that the contractor has contravened consumer legislation, they may take action on your behalf.

THE SMALL CLAIMS COURT

If your claim is for no more than £5,000, use the Small Claims Court which is part of the local County Court. This is relatively informal and neither side is obliged to use a solicitor. If you lose the case, even if the other party uses a solicitor, you cannot be ordered to pay their costs (unless the Court thinks that your claim is unreasonable and a waste of the Court's time or if you fail to attend the hearing). A form should be completed with the help of your adviser and sent to the Court with the appropriate fee. When your case is heard you will have the right to direct questions to the 'defendant' (the contractor) but court time is very limited so work very closely with an adviser to produce direct and concise questions and a coherent case. Make absolutely sure that you have everything carefully documented. Some judges have little patience to listen to a poorly presented case and sometimes let rogue traders off the hook. Local advisers will also know which judges are most sympathetic and may provide useful guidance through the court 'system'.

Once you have received judgment in your favour you should pursue compensation through an order to pay your costs directly from the defendant's bank account. Avoid any action using bailiffs – they are a waste of time.

Information leaflets on the process are available from the courts or from the local TSO or Citizens Advice Bureau. Procedures and fees are slightly different in Scotland and Ireland. Consult the same sources for local procedure. See Appendix 8, page 218 for an example statement and claim form.

Claims in excess of £5,000 should be actioned in the County Court or High Court and legal representation will be required.

Once you have decided to take legal action, curtail any further correspondence with the contractor because this may complicate your claim or delay proceedings. If the contractor writes to you, reply with "I acknowledge your correspondence but I have already instigated proceedings for the reasons previously stated." If you are using a solicitor, ask, in your final letter to the contractor, that any further correspondence be directed to him.

The plaintiff must mitigate his loss

You must take all reasonable steps to keep your costs to a minimum when taking action against a contractor. You are hence obliged to seek competitive quotations for any remedial works. If you cannot live in your house because of the overrun, stay in a reasonable local hotel – not the Ritz.

Finally, you must recognise that in any dispute, even if you win the case, you might not get all you asked for or have all your costs paid.

Chapter 13:

Retentions, Damages and Guarantees

Retentions

It has been customary for many years with larger construction projects for the client to retain a sum of money (usually 2½% to 5%) after the work has been completed. This acts both as an incentive for the contractor to put right any defects that appear and to cover the cost of having minor defects rectified by another contractor should the original contractor default on his guarantee. Some formal contracts for smaller works, even domestic extension work, may include a retention clause.

If you are dealing with a reputable local firm which has been in business for years, it is unlikely that you would need retention as a lever in the event of a defect.

If a retention figure is too significant, it is likely that contractors will increase their prices to cover it. If it is too small, it will be less hassle for the contractor to lose it than do any remedial work. Either way the point is lost.

On any job where interim payments are over £2,000, think about taking a 5% to 10% retention on interim valuations, even if no retention is held after the final payment. This interim retention will keep the balance of power in your hands for the duration of the work and – given that you are no quantity surveyor – should balance out any slight over-valuing by the contractor. Any retention arrangements must be agreed with the contractor at the outset of the contract.

Damages

Many formal contracts include provision for charging the contractor (or deducting from his account) 'damages' if he does not complete the work on time. This is to avoid the necessity of litigation to recover losses. This can be done by stating, in the contract, a maximum sum (which can be agreed between the parties) of so much per week of overrun, that may be deducted from the contractor's account. This is called 'Liquidated Damages'. Alternatively, a clause may be inserted that allows you to deduct 'reasonable damages' for any overrun. As explained elsewhere, this may not cover specific costs of which the contractor may be unaware. These provisions are often referred to as a 'penalty clause', yet damages (compensation) can only be claimed to meet an actual loss. The concept of penalising a contractor is actually void in law and will not be upheld by the courts. With most domestic work, unless there is a specific cost that the client will incur through late completion, damages are hard to justify. On substantial contracts where, for instance, the client is paying to live elsewhere until the work is complete, damages to cover the cost of staying away longer may be reasonable. Only larger contractors are likely to enter into an agreement with a homeowner that includes a Liquidated Damages clause.

Guarantees

Your first guarantee is the legal right to have the work carried out *with reasonable care and skill*. If a defect becomes apparent within a short time, you have a reasonable argument that the workmanship was faulty. With equipment that has been supplied as part of the works, your contractor is your supplier and, again, in law it is his responsibility to deal with it. Guarantees provided by suppliers may need to be 'assigned' to you as the new owner of the material/equipment.

In addition to this basic legal requirement, construction work is traditionally guaranteed for a minimum of 12 months, and frequently longer, against any material or workmanship defects. You should include such a requirement in any documentation that you produce and any standard contracts should have a similar clause.

Written guarantees provided by a contractor or supplier should be clear and unequivocal. If there are any exclusions check them carefully. Apart from malicious damage or 'force majeure' (act of God) there should be few exclusions in a guarantee for construction work. In fact if the 'act of God' is routine – wind, rain, snow to the extremes normally encountered in the geographical area in question – then the construction work should withstand it. For example, a roof on a coastal bungalow should withstand a Force 8 gale. However, a lean-to roof against a house in Cornwall might not be expected to hold up under 15 inches of snow.

If a contractor fails to honour his guarantee within a reasonable time, you can engage another firm to carry out the remedial work but you must write to the contractor informing him that you intend to take this action, giving him a further opportunity to fix the problem himself (see Sample Letter 10, page 212).

You can, legally, only insist that your original contractor reimburses you the 'reasonable' cost of putting the matter right. You ensure that the cost is 'reasonable' by obtaining three prices. Of course if the work is a matter of extreme urgency you would not be expected to incur delay in order to demonstrate that the price was reasonable.

If your original contractor refuses to reimburse you or argues about the price, speak to your local Trading Standards Office or a solicitor. If the contractor goes bust your guarantee will be worthless so, as indicated earlier, insurance backed guarantees are preferable.

LATENT DEFECTS

Some defects in work do not become apparent until after the 12 month guarantee has elapsed. A typical example may be foundations or structural elements where additional loading imposed by severe weather, or changes to soil moisture content, can mean that the structure is not fully 'tested' within the guarantee period. In these cases, the expiry of the guarantee should not prevent the client from having recourse to the contractor if the problem is attributable to faulty design or workmanship.

Action must be brought within two years of reasonable knowledge of the defect. So even if the first sign is just a small crack or a door no longer closing properly, report it immediately, in writing, to the contractor. If the contractor is slow to admit liability you will need to involve a third party and pursue the matter with a surveyor or a solicitor who specialises in construction related matters.

Chapter 14:

A Final Word

To cover every potential difficulty that the homeowner might face in the course of employing tradesmen could cover several volumes, most of which would be very tedious to the majority of readers. I have endeavoured, with this book, to cover the subjects that are most likely to arise and to give sufficient understanding of the processes. If the entire work could be summarised in five key points, they would be these:

❖ Be as clear as you can about what you want.
❖ Base your selection of a contractor on how sure you are that he will do a decent job, not just on his price.
❖ Avoid deposits and pay only for work completed to your satisfaction.
❖ Pay attention to what the contractor is doing.
❖ Be prepared to act or seek advice as soon as you suspect something is not right.

What most surprises those in the construction industry about many of the construction horror stories that come to light is how things were allowed to get 'that bad'. There is simply no reason to put up with a non-performing contractor or to pay for something unless it is completed to a good standard.

Many homeowners would think little of spending an extra £200 on brass doorknobs or a new fireplace, yet so many delay spending that amount on a surveyor or a consulting engineer in order to check some work of dubious quality.

I hope that this book has enabled you to be a fair judge of what is and what is not reasonable in the context of construction work and, where you are unsure, to seek appropriate advice.

Of course 'reasonable' means different things to different people and I am sure that there are many contractors who could write a small volume on dealing with difficult customers. Construction work is complex. Unlike a car or a washing machine, which would have gone through various prototype stages before going into production, every construction project is a 'one off'. Equally, when you buy a finished object, you can expect a fixed price, whereas a quotation for construction work is only the price you will pay if there are no deviations from the original concept.

A fuller understanding of these issues should also enable you to be a 'good client' and to realise that contractors, architects, planners and engineers are all human and every day deal with slight variations within their field of speciality. Also, you need to understand that bricks, timber and concrete are not precision-engineered materials. If you are a perfectionist, you may find complete satisfaction hard to attain. If, however, you simply do your best and expect everyone else to do likewise, you have every right to be satisfied and are more likely to be so.

Appendix 1:

General Conditions

The following 'General conditions' show a number of clauses that should afford you some basic legal protection and would be understood by most contractors. You are free to use these conditions without reference to the publishers but they are offered as a suggestion only. It is up to you to be comfortable with the words and intentions and if you have any doubts you should seek advice.

The term 'client' is used in the conditions. You may feel that this third person reference creates a useful formality and wish to adopt it. Alternatively you may think it sounds pompous, in which case you can replace it with 'I' and 'my'.

*delete/add to as appropriate

GENERAL CONDITIONS

This document has been produced in order to obtain fair competitive prices for the work and to provide a guide to the client's requirements with the intention of preventing misunderstandings and clarifying responsibilities.

1. CONTRACT DOCUMENTATION

The following documents will form the basis of any contract resulting from the client's acceptance of the contractor's offer.

*   These conditions

The designer's specification/the client's brief
Drawings/sketches reference numbers . . .
The contractor's offer
The client's letter of acceptance

2. CONTRACTOR'S EXPERTISE

The client assumes that the contractor has the necessary expertise, experience and technical knowledge to carry out the work detailed in a proper manner and a returned price will constitute an assertion that this is the case. Where the contractor has agreed to carry out design and drawing work the contractor shall take full responsibility for all elements of the design, structural integrity and accuracy of all measurements. The contractor, where the work includes design, shall indemnify the client against any defects arising from his design, for a period of no less than 10 years.

3. DRAWINGS AND SPECIFICATION (where brief is supplied by client)

The contractor shall understand that the brief is not exhaustive in its detail but is a guide to the client's requirements. The contractor shall allow in his price for all work that would reasonably be required in order to provide a complete and finished job to good standards and to meet the essence of the client's requirements. The same shall apply to any drawings provided by the client. In the event of any conflict or apparent error or lack of detail within the documents or drawings, the contractor is to allow for the most expensive option when pricing, or to indicate in his tender the assumptions made and query the matter with the client before commencing work.

OR

3. DRAWINGS AND SPECIFICATION (where a designer is responsible for the specification)

The contractor shall understand that the specification/ drawings are not necessarily exhaustive in their detail and he shall allow in his price for all work that would reasonably be required in order to provide a complete and finished job to good standards and to meet the essence of the specification. In the event of any conflict or apparent error or lack of detail within the documents or drawings, the contractor is to allow for the most expensive option when pricing or to indicate in his tender the assumptions made and query the matter with the client before commencing work.

4. SITE SURVEY

The contractor is deemed to have carried out any necessary inspection of the property and to have taken any dimensions required in order that his price accurately reflects the amount of work involved. Claims for unforeseeable work will not be entertained where the work could reasonably have been anticipated by thorough survey. Any areas where the contractor feels that unforeseen work may arise, i.e. where prior inspection is impossible, should be highlighted in the quotation.

5. STATUTORY REQUIREMENTS

All work and materials must comply with the Building Regulations and the requirements of the Building Control officer. The contractor is to arrange any inspections required by the Local Authority.

6. HEALTH & SAFETY AND PROTECTION

The contractor shall be entirely responsible for health and safety of all operatives and take all practical steps to ensure the safety of people living at the site address, any visitors to the property and the public whilst working on the property. The contractor shall also be responsible for the care and protection of the client's property, the new construction and any materials and equipment supplied for the works. The contractor shall have valid public liability insurance to cover all conceivable eventualities, evidence of which will be required prior to commencement of any work.

7. 'APPROVALS'

Any approval by the client of drawings produced by the contractor shall be approval in principle only. No approval will negate the responsibility of the contractor to apply his expertise and meet all elements of the specification/the client's brief and requirements for good working practice.

8. WORKMANSHIP, MATERIALS AND GUARANTEE

All work shall be carried out in accordance with good working practice and shall provide a good standard of finish. All materials shall be new unless otherwise agreed with the client and, where visible on completion of the work, of appearance agreed with the client. Only materials suitable for their purpose shall be used. The contractor should advise the client if he believes that any specified element is unsuitable. All workmanship and materials shall be guaranteed for a minimum period of 12 months. This guarantee shall not prejudice the client's position in law or affect specific guarantees given on relevant items of work or the right of the client to make any claim in respect of latent defects.

9. GENERAL CONDUCT AND SECURITY

The contractor shall carry out all work in a manner that minimises inconvenience to the client's household and neighbours whilst maintaining progress. All tools and equipment shall be neatly stored at the end of each working day and dustsheets, screens, boarding, etc., shall be employed to minimise the spread of site dust and debris. The contractor shall be responsible for the security of his plant and all materials. All rubbish shall be regularly removed and skips, accessible to the street, are to be covered when not in use. The contractor shall remove and store/lock any ladders when not in use and take other necessary precautions to minimise the risk to security whilst the work is in progress.

10. PROGRAMME

The contractor shall, upon receipt of written acceptance of his tender, produce a programme of works indicating anticipated start and finish dates and shall progress the works accordingly. The contractor shall write to the client advising of any delays indicating the reason. In the event that the works are insufficiently progressed, without good reason and it becomes clear that the completion date will not be met, the client will issue a default notice. If no substantial progress is made or reasonable explanation given within 14 days, the client reserves the right to terminate the contract forthwith and have the work completed by others. Any costs arising will be deducted from the contractor's account. Action may be taken to recover any losses in excess of the amount outstanding. If the contractor is unable to start work within four weeks of the date agreed prior to the receipt of an order, the client reserves the right to cancel the contract.

11. VARIATIONS

The client reserves the right to vary the specified works by addition, omission or alteration. Any variations, whether initiated by the client or resulting from occurrence during the course of the work, must be agreed in writing. The contract conditions shall apply to any variations as if they were part of this enquiry. Where variations are likely to increase the price of the work, the contractor is to submit a price for the extra work or agree with the client the method of pricing before the work proceeds. Extra work carried out without written agreement may not be paid for.

12. MAIN CONTRACTOR'S RESPONSIBILITY

Where the contractor who is the party to this agreement is employing specialist trades to carry out part of the works he shall remain responsible for all subcontracted works as if they were his own, and for any necessary co-ordination and the timely passing of any instructions. The client's permission must be obtained before any element of the work is subcontracted.

13. DISPUTES

This document shall be considered as a contract in English law. In the event of a dispute, other than a breach of contract, the parties shall agree on a suitable mediator or arbitrator. If the parties cannot agree on a suitable arbitrator, an independent arbitrator shall be appointed by the Chartered Institute of Arbitrators and the parties shall be bound by the appointed arbitrator's adjudication and his apportionment of costs.

14. PAYMENT

Payment will be made monthly starting on the 30th day after commencement, until the work is within one month of the agreed completion date. Further payments prior to the final account will be at the discretion of the client. Where a Building Control 'Final Certificate' is applicable, final payment will only be made on receipt of this document.

Appendix 2:

Sample Brief

The following is a simple brief for the conversion of a small bedroom into an en-suite bathroom.

CONSTRUCTION BRIEF FOR

The conversion of a bedroom to an en-suite bathroom at 42 Wildview Road, Wimblethorn, Beds.

PRELIMINARY ISSUES

Access to the house will be available throughout the contract period and the contractor is free to use the downstairs WC and electric kettle. Arrangements will be made concerning keys. The outside tap shall be used where water is required for the works. We are a non-smoking household and all operatives are requested to observe this.

OUTLINE

The existing small bedroom (bedroom 5 on the plan) is to be converted into an en-suite bathroom for bedroom 1. The work is to include all building, plumbing, electrical and finishing works.

There is a leak from the roof above the bedroom and this is to be repaired before finishes are commenced. It is believed that the cause of the leak is a failure of the flashing around the chimney.

THE WORK REQUIRED

1. Carefully remove door and architrave from existing bedroom 5 entrance and set aside for re-use. Block up doorway with 100mm studwork, 12.5mm plasterboard and mineral wool insulation fill. Finish with plaster skim to finish level with existing wall lines.

2. Create new doorway between bedroom 5 and master bedroom. Position as shown on drawing. This is a solid wall and adequate provision is to be made to transfer any structural load from the roof. See attached structural engineer's report and adhere to the recommendations.

3. Fit new door lining, jamb and architrave from bedroom 5. Re-hang door from bedroom 5 in new opening. Use existing ironmongery.

4. Remove existing metal framed window (in bedroom 5) and install new timber framed double glazed window with top section openable. New window to have obscured glass and to meet current building regulation. (Please provide literature or sample of proposed window.)

5. I have selected a bathroom suite, taps, fitted cupboards, etc. and listed the details on the attached schedule. Please offer a separate price for supplying this equipment.

6. Install bathroom equipment and furniture as shown on the attached plan.

7. Run waste pipework to new black PVC stack and connect the stack via underground pipework to the existing manhole.

8. Supply and install new 180 litre hotwater cylinder in place of existing and connect all existing pipework (cylinder to comply with Building Regulations 'Part L'). Run hot and coldwater services in appropriate sizes from new cylinder and coldwater tank. Run a

separate cold supply from the coldwater tank to the bath/shower mixer. Fit isolating valves to all taps to allow for maintenance.

9. Remove existing radiator and pipework connections in bedroom 5. Fit new towel radiator (as attached literature) in position shown on drawing and run heating pipework to suit.
10. Carry out electrical work as shown on the drawing including disconnection and removal of existing socket outlets, installation of lighting and shaver points. Install new ceiling lights (fittings supplied).
11. Carry out wall tiling as shown on the drawing. (Tiles from "Tiles 'R' Us", High Street, Wimblethorn, ref TRU 670/azure.)
12. Allow for all making good around new doorway and new window and any moulding, filling or other finishing required to make the bathroom complete.
13. Allow for replacement of existing flashing to chimney and any necessary work to adjacent roof tiles.

All work is to be carried out to the highest standard and in accordance with Building Regulations and Institute of Plumbing standards. Electrical work shall be carried out by an NICEIC registered electrician in accordance with IEE Regulations.

The above is an outline of what is required but the work is to provide everything necessary for a fully functional bathroom with the exception of final painting and floor laying.

Please provide your price broken down as follows:

1. Building works including tiling.
2. Plumbing works.
3. Electrical work.
4. New window.
5. Sanitary ware, etc.
6. Bathroom fitted units.
7. Roof repair.

Please provide labour rate and material percentage addition that will be used if the roof work is more complex than anticipated.

Appendix 3:

General Construction Notes and Typical Specification Clauses

The notes in bold type are **suggested** general standards that you may wish to include in your brief.

GENERAL BUILDING

Overall construction quality is a difficult thing to pin down but it is useful to have something in your brief or terms that requires an 'acceptable' level of workmanship. To make 'acceptable' more specific (i.e. to avoid having to engage a third party to determine what is acceptable) you could quote BS 8000 which is the British Standards Code of Practice for workmanship in construction and covers most types of work:

– **Work to be carried out in accordance with BS 8000 "Workmanship on Building Sites" parts 1-16 (where appropriate to the work).**

This will ensure that good standards are enshrined in your contract so breach of standards will mean breach of contract. The negative side of this is that few builders will have a copy of the BS document (the whole set costs £300) so through concern about incurring costs due to contravention of some minor point, they may not accept it. Also, if you don't have a copy it will be difficult to enforce.

FOUNDATIONS

–   Must be of a design, size and depth adequate for a) the structure that they are supporting, b) the soil type and c) must be to the approval of the Building Control Department.

The type, width, thickness and depth of any foundation for a new structure or extension must be designed to suit the load of the structure and the ground that it is to sit on. Soil types, nearby trees, etc. will affect this. Unless your contractor is also responsible for the design, a structural engineer or architect should be engaged to detail this element of the work or approve the contractor's drawings.

EXTERNAL FABRIC GENERALLY

–   The external building fabric is to be constructed in a manner and with appropriate materials to ensure that heat transfer, prevention of moisture penetration and all other aspects are fully in accordance with current Building Regulations and good working practice.
–   The contractor shall ensure that the Building Control officer is notified (where applicable) in order that mandatory inspections are carried out. The client shall be informed of all such arrangements.

THERMAL PERFORMANCE

The Building Regulations require that new construction, including extensions and substantial repairs, meet a standard for thermal performance. 'Approved Document Part L' shows a 'U value' for each element of the building fabric i.e. walls, floor, roof, windows, etc. (The 'U' value is the rate at which heat will be lost through that building element in watts per square metre, for each degree centigrade difference between inside and outside temperature.) A wall with a U value of 0.45 will lose more heat than a wall with a U value of 0.3.

Over the years, these figures have been reduced in order to reduce energy consumption and carbon dioxide emissions from heat generating equipment. The figures from the 2002 edition show the following (figures apply to homes with gas or oil central heating):

Walls	U = 0.35
Floors	U = 0.25
Pitched roof	U = 0.16 (insulation between joists)
	U = 0.2 (insulation between rafters)
Flat roofs	U = 0.25
Windows and doors	U = 2.0 (timber or PVC frames)
	U = 2.2 (metal frames)

It is possible to 'trade off' elements so that, for example, if a proposed window does not comply, additional roof insulation may be added so that the overall heat loss is no more than it would have been if every element complied.

GROUND FLOORS

There are different floor types. Solid floors (as shown in Fig. 13a) are generally a 75mm sand and cement 'screed' on concrete (usually 100-150mm) on hardcore on firmed ground with damp proofing membrane and insulation sandwiched in between. 'Suspended' floors (as shown in Fig. 13b) are generally timber floor joists or concrete beams attached to the walls and suspended above a weak mix of concrete laid on the ground. Insulation must be incorporated, usually as mineral wool between timber floor joists or as foam type slabs above 'block & beam' floors. See Appendix 5.

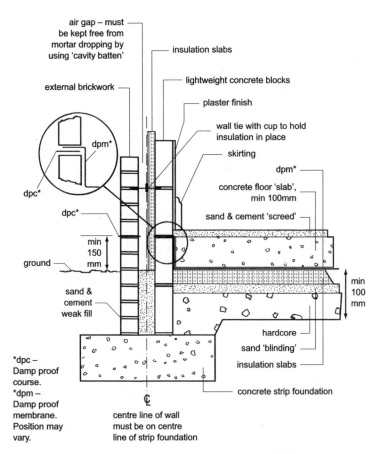

air gap – must be kept free from mortar dropping by using 'cavity batten'

insulation slabs

external brickwork

lightweight concrete blocks

plaster finish

wall tie with cup to hold insulation in place

skirting

dpm*

dpm*

concrete floor 'slab', min 100mm

dpc*

sand & cement 'screed'

dpc*

min 150 mm

ground

min 100 mm

sand & cement weak fill

hardcore

sand 'blinding'

insulation slabs

*dpc – Damp proof course.
*dpm – Damp proof membrane. Position may vary.

concrete strip foundation

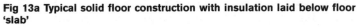

centre line of wall must be on centre line of strip foundation

Fig 13a Typical solid floor construction with insulation laid below floor 'slab'

EXTERNAL WALLS

The external appearance of new walls is the critical factor provided that insulation standards are met. You may wish any new brickwork to match the existing (local authority Planning may insist upon this at the front of the property). You should ask the contractor to provide a sample panel or

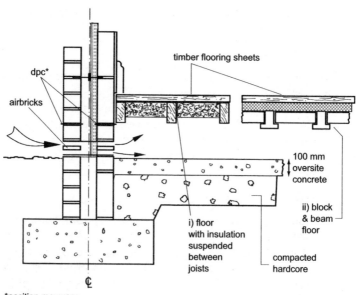

*position may vary

Fig 13b Suspended floor construction

contact brick manufacturers and ask for literature. You must see actual samples if matching existing (there will be more different brick types than you think).

Where facing brickwork is required, insulated cavity walls (brick, insulated cavity, block work, finishing plaster) are the most common but there is a variety of alternative arrangements. Construction using a single masonry skin or weatherproof boarding, with thick insulation slabs and boarding fitted to a timber frame (known as 'timber frame construction'), is becoming more popular for new housing and is sometimes used with extensions. This construction must incorporate an uninterrupted damp proof membrane to prevent moisture penetration to the timber. Solid construction, e.g. block work and insulation, may meet insulation requirements but in exposed areas an air gap is generally required as a precaution against moisture penetration.

BRICKWORK GENERALLY

Where adjoining an existing wall, horizontal mortar courses should align with the existing.

Bricks with mixed and variegated appearance should be laid in a manner that ensures an overall appearance free from patches of the same colour. Good bricklaying is an art – not all 'jack of all trades' builders are good bricklayers.

POINTING AND REPOINTING

Mortar should be raked out to a depth of about 15mm and loose material removed with a course brush. Pointing can be finished in different ways: in a flush, angled or recessed manner. The style of pointing should match the existing where repairs are carried out. With new brickwork the pointing can be selected to suit the required style of finish. With reclaimed or handmade bricks that are uneven in appearance, a neat flush or angled mortar line can (in my opinion) make the wall look like a badly built inglenook chimney breast. These look better with a recessed joint so that the uneven or weathered character of the bricks is maintained.

Where repointing, inspect the brickwork with the contractor to agree the precise area to be repointed before a price is offered. Allow for a slightly larger area than that of the loose mortar because mortar that appears sound may be disturbed when the work is done.

ROOFS

Roofing is a trade that attracts cowboys like happy hour at the local saloon! Safely out of sight, all manner of botched jobs can be carried out. Try to obtain recommendations when finding a roofer or select a contractor registered with the National Federation of Roofing Contractors. Always discuss the materials to be used and inspect the work where practical and safe to do so.

Pitched roofs are always preferable to flat roofs because they last longer. They are, however, more expensive and in some cases, where there is a height restriction, only a flat roof can be accommodated.

There are two principal types of flat roofs: the 'cold deck' type with insulation fitted between the joists and below the 'deck' – the term for timber sheeting – and the warm deck roof, which has rigid insulation slabs fitted on top of the deck. Cold deck roofs must have about 50mm of air space above the insulation and some form of through ventilation to avoid condensation. With increasing insulation require- ments, this can mean that the depth of timbers is based on accommodating insulation rather than structural strength. Traditional flat roofing is finished with three layers of bitumen based roofing felt with hot bitumen bonded over- laps. The life expectancy of this arrangement is five to ten years. Technology has moved on and there is now a range of 'elastomeric', fibreglass and other roof coverings which far outlast ordinary felt. Some of these have guarantees of up to 25 years. Either research and specify a system or ask contractors to propose a system and then check it out. You must demand that any proprietary system is installed fully in accordance with the manufacturer's instructions, in order to be covered by the guarantee.

The roof decking should be plywood or roofing grade chipboard (type C4, which is water resistant and has red and green stripes applied to it at manufacture, to distinguish it from ordinary chipboard which is not water resistant).

The general method for pitched roof constructions is for tiles or slates on timber battens which are fixed to the rafters through a sheet of lightweight felt. The length of overhang (one row over the next) and the frequency of fixing will generally be recommended by the tile manufac- turer for a given pitch (slope) of roof.

Insulation for a roof space is usually mineral wool blanket placed between the joists, i.e. sitting on the plasterboard ceiling below. With a loft conversion, any remaining unused roof void may be insulated this way but the occupied areas will need to have either: mineral wool insulation fitted between the rafters, insulating boarding outside the rafters (possible with a new roof) or insulating boarding internally (in which case the timbers must be ventilated). Incorporating sufficient insulation to suit Building Regulations and having adequate ventilation to prevent dampness in roof timbers is becoming a bit of a challenge and the contractor's proposed methods should be verified.

Dormer windows should not have their flat roofs (if applicable) or sides covered with roofing felt. Exposure and difficulties with access for replacement make this inappropriate and other, more durable, materials should be used. Fig. 14 (overleaf) shows a section through eaves, window opening and the arrangement around a flat roof extension.

WEATHERING

Where a roof connects to an adjacent wall there must be no water penetration at the joint between the roof and the wall. This is achieved, traditionally, by using lead, zinc or proprietary materials secured into a mortar joint in the brickwork above the intersection and run down onto the roof. This is known as 'flashing' (see Fig. 21, page 204). Roofing felt is sometimes used but this is inferior to lead. Where a flat roof has an asphalt covering, this may be run up the wall into a mortar joint to act as flashing. Bitumastic flashing tape is available but this is not suitable for anything more substantial than a lean-to roof on a shed or carport. See Fig. 14, overleaf.

INTERNAL WALLS

If internal walls are to be load bearing, they will generally be constructed from block work although there are other methods. They will also require proper foundations.

Other internal walls will generally be 'studwork' walls. The 'studs' are usually 100mm x 50mm timber (although metal studwork can be used) at about 400mm centres. The

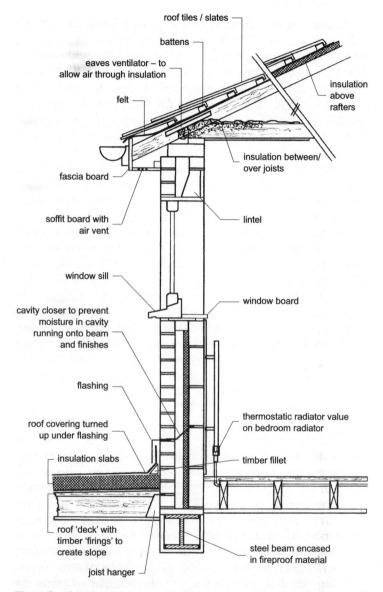

roof tiles / slates

battens

eaves ventilator – to allow air through insulation

felt

insulation above rafters

fascia board

insulation between/ over joists

soffit board with air vent

lintel

window sill

window board

cavity closer to prevent moisture in cavity running onto beam and finishes

flashing

thermostatic radiator value on bedroom radiator

roof covering turned up under flashing

insulation slabs

timber fillet

roof 'deck' with timber 'firings' to create slope

steel beam encased in fireproof material

joist hanger

Fig 14 Section through eaves, window opening and arrangement around flat roof to extension

studs are cross-braced at intervals and the wall covered with plasterboard. Cross bracing should line up with the edge of the plasterboard (generally 2.4m x 1.2m sheets) so that all four sides are supported. Fitting insulation blanket in the space between the studs will deaden the sound and prevent the wall sounding like those in a cheap hotel. Solid (brickwork or blockwork) walls will always provide a better barrier to sound, so where this is important you may wish to request solid partitions. On upper floors where this is not structurally possible (because of the additional weight), ask the contractor to suggest alternative acoustic boarding in place of ordinary plasterboard. You may need to do some of your own research on this.

Instead of a plaster finish, boards may be left unplastered with the joints taped and filled. This is called 'dry lining'. If you intend to wallpaper the walls, a plaster finish will be preferable because paper cannot easily be removed from a dry lining board. A plaster finish is also preferable in a bathroom. (The surface of plasterboard is paper.) An alternative in both cases would be proprietary dry lining boarding which has a harder and more water resistant surface.

Beams and Lintels

- **All openings in masonry walls are to be fitted with appropriate lintels or arches. Structural steelwork shall be carefully selected and sized for its purpose and the load being taken. Where steelwork is detailed on a drawing or a structural engineer's schedule, the precise instructions given must be followed.**
- **Beams and lintels shall be correctly installed with the correct bearing either side of the opening. Bearing shall be on engineering bricks or dense concrete padstones where the load on the walls would exceed the brick or block**

strength. Lintels and beams shall have loads evenly distributed unless designed for uneven loading.

To support the structure over doors and windows, contractors will generally use 'off the shelf' lintels and manufacturers' charts will aid correct selection. Where steel beams are used to support a wall above, the selection is more critical and must be done by a structural engineer. Calculations and selection of steelwork must be approved by the Building Control officer.

The purpose of a beam is to transfer the load above to the adjacent walls. The length of a beam or lintel that overhangs (i.e. rests on the walls at both ends of an opening) is called the 'bearing' and it must be at least 150mm. With a wide opening, the load at the bearing points can be beyond that which will crush ordinary brick/block work. The beam must either be increased in length to spread the weight over a greater area or must sit on a 'padstone'. This is a block of concrete (sometimes dense 'engineering' bricks are used) that will not be crushed under the load of the beam but will transfer that load over a wider area of less dense ordinary masonry (see Fig. 15, showing a beam sitting on a padstone).

The necessity for a padstone will depend on the load that is being carried by the bearing surface. For a single small opening, a window, etc., ordinary masonry can usually take the weight.

Where there is an existing load above a new beam, as with an opening to a new extension, the load will be supported temporarily (before the hole is cut). This is usually done with adjustable props. The space between the top of the beam and the masonry above must be packed with mortar. It is important that there is minimal shrinkage in this mortar, which normally happens when mortar dries out, otherwise the wall above will 'drop' onto the beam. 'Dry packing' is the term used to describe a damp, sharp sand and cement mix (ratio 3:1) used for this purpose. Water should be added to the mix but only such that, when squeezed in the hand, it does not emit water but does not crumble. The mix should be rammed hard into the space and allowed to dry fully for 24 hours before removing the supports. An alternative is the use of an expanding additive that will counteract the shrinkage but this needs to be mixed and applied very carefully and is more difficult to check.

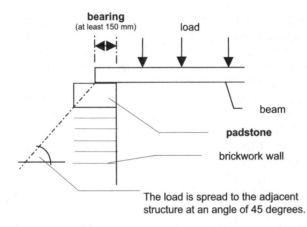

The load is spread to the adjacent structure at an angle of 45 degrees.

Fig 15 Beam sitting on a 'padstone'

Steelwork distorts if it is exposed to extreme heat and this can cause premature collapse of a structure in the event of a fire. Protection is usually achieved by encasing the steelwork with a fireproof board – not with MDF or any other timber! If internal exposed steelwork is part of a design feature, intumescent paint can be used. This is a coating which, when exposed to high temperature, expands to many times its normal volume and provides temporary fire protection to the surface of the steel.

STRUCTURAL TIMBERWORK

Structural timbers should be kiln dried and pre-treated with preservative. They should be free from excessive twisting or bowing and should be protected from inclement weather when stored on site. Timber members – joists, beams, purlins, etc. should be from single lengths of timber; joints part way along these members are unacceptable.

VENTILATION

a) To habitable spaces.
    Whilst a leaky structure is difficult and expensive to heat, an airtight space is unhealthy and can cause condensation. The Building Regulations set out current requirements and methods of ventilation. Kitchens and bathrooms should be fitted with extractor fans and all other rooms should have 'trickle vents' fitted to windows or airbricks, etc. (Building Regulations are not retrospective but will apply to most new work.)
b) To void areas.
    Roof spaces and suspended floors are cold places in winter. Water vapour (the moisture that is generally contained in air) moves from warm heated spaces to these cold areas and can form condensation because (in simple terms) the vapour turns back into water when it is cooled or encounters a cold surface. Where structural timbers are in cold places these places need to be ventilated to keep the timbers dry.

WINDOWS AND GLAZING

New and replacement windows should be double glazed, argon gas filled, and have 'thermal breaks' (between cold external and warm internal parts of the frame) to suit the 'U values' required in the Building Regulations (see page 166 under Thermal Performance regarding 'trade offs'). You will have the option of fully or partially openable. Consider fire exits – particularly on upper floors. Consider security – particularly on ground floor windows and on those facing across a flat roof (air vents are a particular weak spot). Some manufacturers have given more consideration to this than others, although contractors may just supply the cheapest windows they can get, unless you ask for samples or do your own investigations and specify a particular type.

Glazing less than 800mm from the floor (1500mm if within 300mm of a door) must be safety glass (toughened or laminated). Children are particularly at risk from running into low level glazing (not surprisingly).

DOORS

There is a wide range of internal and external doors from which to choose. External doors, glazed solid or part glazed, tend to be of reasonably solid construction but must comply with Building Regulations for thermal performance. UPVC doors are maintenance free and keep their appearance very well – unfortunately it is the appearance of a UPVC door! The construction of some UPVC doors is such that they have very high thresholds that are easy to trip over. Better designs have lower thresholds with the base of the frame fitted in place of, rather than on top of, the existing threshold – so shop around.

With internal doors, it is very much a case of 'you get what you pay for'. The cheapest available are those with a cardboard honeycomb 'matrix' core and a softwood frame. They come in a variety of designs with moulded panels. Better quality versions have thicker frames making the fitting of locks simpler and providing a heavier feel. Solid timber panelled doors will both feel and be more expensive.

It is important to research this element and specify what you want, or the contractor will fit the cheapest available.

Solid, panelled timber doors are available from reclamation yards. This may be a useful source if you are trying to match existing period doors or restore the property to a period style.

DECORATION

- **The contractor shall ensure that all paintwork, varnishing, etc. is carried out after adequate preparation, as recommended by paint manufacturers and good practice, and that products are appropriate for the purpose for which they are used. All timberwork shall be rubbed down between coats and topcoats protected from dust. Paint finishes and colours to be agreed with client before application.**
- **External paintwork shall be microporous or other external quality paint with preparation and application in full accordance with the manufacturer's instructions.**

Watch out for extreme weather conditions – most paints should not be applied when it is too hot, too cold or when it is wet. Talk to the contractor about masking or removing fixtures and fittings: satellite dishes, etc.

SERVICES

GUTTERING AND DOWNPIPES

PVC is the usual material used nowadays but this may not be allowed on a listed building or in a conservation area. If replacing existing guttering, check the condition of the fascia and soffit boards (see Appendix 5, pages 200 and 203). Replacement of this, traditionally timber, boarding with UPVC panels is the latest in quick fit package refurbishments. It is frequently offered with new guttering but is not always necessary. The benefit of UPVC is zero maintenance. With ventilated roof spaces soffit boards should be fitted with air vents and the corners of UPVC panels should be strengthened with timber inserts.

Guttering should be supported using purpose made clips affixed to the fascia board. It should generally be laid to fall and connect to downpipes that discharge over a gully or connect directly into the underground drainage. No sanitaryware may connect to rainwater pipes.

WASTE PIPEWORK

– **The wastewater installation shall comply in all respects with Institute of Plumbing guidelines, relevant British Standards and Codes of Practice and the requirements of the Building Control inspector.**

Waste pipework, which is generally plastic, should be laid to a fall of between 20 and 90mm per metre run and then connect to a waste 'stack' (a vertical pipe min 100mm diameter that connects to the drain) or directly to the drain. Wastes from all appliances (basins, baths and showers) must be trapped to prevent smells rising from the waste system. To avoid traps being siphoned out by the action of running water there is a maximum length of pipe for a given diameter – hence a maximum distance from each sink, bath, etc., from the waste stack. These distances are: 3 metres for 40mm diameter pipe, 4 metres for 50mm diameter pipe. WCs may be up to 6 metres from a stack but must have 100mm diameter pipework. The exception to this is where a special pump is used (see Chapter 3, page 33).

The waste 'stack' must either rise to above the roof level (to ensure ventilation and avoid creating a vacuum) or, where this is impractical, be fitted with an 'air admittance valve'.

Waste pipework below ground must be either a

heavy-duty plastic pipe, that is distinguished from others by being a red clay colour, or actual clay piping. No underground pipe may join another below ground unless there is access to the joint via a manhole or from a 'roddable* access'. This is to ensure that all sections of underground pipework can be cleared in the event of a blockage. If no existing manhole is available or capable of taking a new connection, a new manhole may be required. The Building Control officer will want to inspect this.

New waste systems should be tested. Above ground, an air test is generally used. Below ground drainage will be either air tested or filled with water (to a maximum height of 2m). If the level of water or air pressure (max. 2.8 lb/sq. in. or 0.19 bar) does not fall for about 10 minutes, the pipework should be free from leaks.

Where drainage pipework runs through a foundation wall it should either run through an opening with a lintel above or via a special coupling built into the wall.

Fig. 16 shows a typical arrangement for rain and waste water pipework.

*Access panel or fitting through which drain clearing rods can be inserted.

HOT AND COLD WATER SERVICES

–   Hot and cold water services shall be installed using 'Table X' copper tube and shall be sized to ensure that all appliances receive good flow under all conditions. Pipework sizing, materials and installation shall be in accordance with modern good practice and the guidelines issued by the Institute of Plumbing.

The traditional material for water services is copper although plastics are becoming more popular.

In order to provide adequate flows to all outlets, pipework must be correctly sized. Bathrooms are generally piped with 22mm pipes (hot and cold) to the bath and

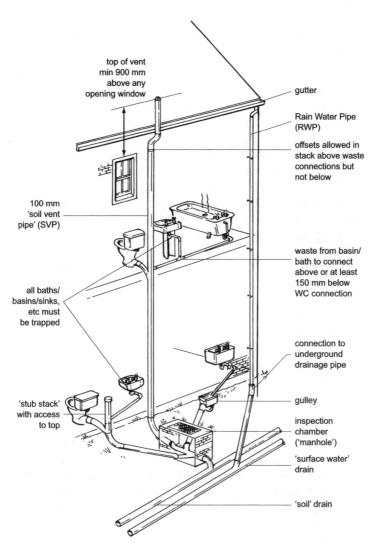

Fig 16 Waste and rainwater system

15mm to the washbasin. The hot tap at a kitchen sink should be piped in 22mm. Cold water mains pipework in most homes only needs to be in 15mm regardless of the appliance being served and the kitchen sink should always be fed from the main.

Shower mixers may require 15mm or 22mm supplies so check the manufacturer's information. Some mixers will only work well if supplied via a pump. In order to avoid scalding, if someone else uses a nearby cold tap and the water pressure available is reduced, install a separate cold supply to a shower from the cold water tank.

The above should only be treated as guidelines. Much will depend on the plumbing layout in your house. Any new additional bathroom using these sizes should have the pipes run separately from the water tank and the hot water cylinder, not just branched from an existing supply to another bathroom. Some loss of pressure to one tap when another is opened is difficult to avoid but it should be minimal. If water from one tap turns to a trickle when another is opened it means that the pipework is under-sized.

See note about electrical 'bonding' on page 188.

CENTRAL HEATING

–   **Pipework shall be copper tube to BS 2871 table X with purpose made capillary fittings. All pipework shall be run neatly and adequately clipped to prevent noise. The pipework shall be fitted with adequate venting and draining facility.**

–   **The boiler, flue and gas pipework shall be installed by a CORGI registered engineer in accordance with BS 5440 and the manufacturer's instructions. Electrical work shall be in accordance with current IEE Regulations.**

– **Radiators shall be sized to achieve 21 deg. C. in reception rooms and bathrooms and 18 deg. C. in the remainder of the house when it is –2 deg. C. outside.***
The system shall be fully pumped with time and temperature control linked to the boiler to prevent cycling** (as required by Building Regulations Approved Document Part L).

* Appropriate for Southern England. If you live in the Midlands or further north, a lower external temperature will be more appropriate. Local installers can advise on this. Systems are not generally designed to maintain normal room temperatures at extreme conditions that will only be experienced for a few days every other year; it would simply be uneconomical.

** Unnecessary repeated boiler firing to satisfy boiler thermostat, when room temperatures are adequate.

Traditionally, copper pipework is used for central heating. Much will depend upon the requirements of the property, but the following are points to note:

The best position for radiators is on outside walls and under windows. Some contractors favour back to back on internal walls but this is to save pipework regardless of any other reason given. You may not feel the benefit of this saving but you will feel the cold draught as it runs down the window and across the floor. Purpose made foil panels can be fitted behind radiators on external walls to reduce the direct loss through the wall.

Boilers should be judged on efficiency and reliability. Avoid makes that few merchants are familiar with; parts may be scarce. Boilers that 'modulate' to suit demand will be more efficient. High efficiency boilers cost less to run and boilers are now graded for running costs the same as refrigerators. Merchants can provide information on alternative boilers or, if you have access to the Internet, www.sedbuk.com shows comparative efficiencies for all domestic boilers in common use. At the top of the league tables at around 86-90 per cent (seasonal efficiency) you

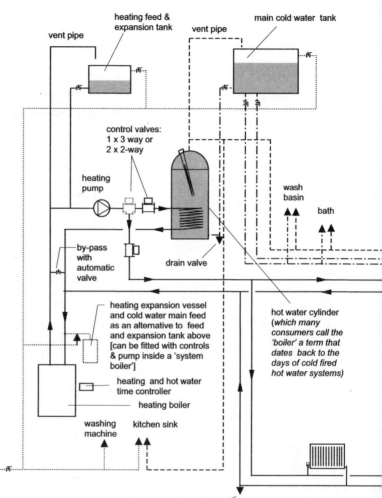

Fig 17a Heating and hot and cold water services, with hot and cold storage

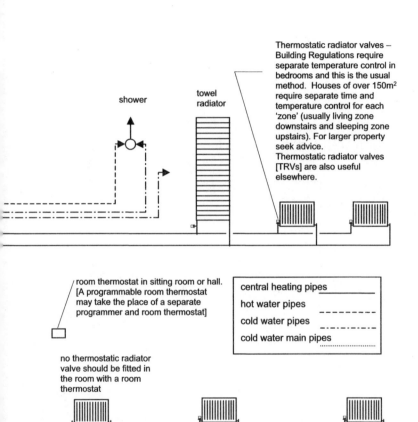

Thermostatic radiator valves – Building Regulations require separate temperature control in bedrooms and this is the usual method. Houses of over 150m² require separate time and temperature control for each 'zone' (usually living zone downstairs and sleeping zone upstairs). For larger property seek advice.
Thermostatic radiator valves [TRVs] are also useful elsewhere.

shower

towel radiator

room thermostat in sitting room or hall. [A programmable room thermostat may take the place of a separate programmer and room thermostat]

no thermostatic radiator valve should be fitted in the room with a room thermostat

| central heating pipes |
| hot water pipes |
| cold water pipes |
| cold water main pipes |

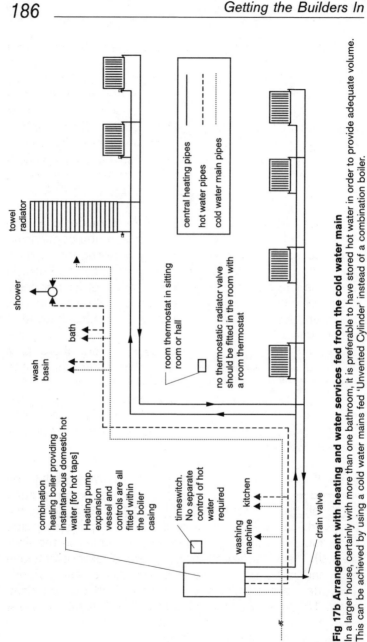

Fig 17b Arrangement with heating and water services fed from the cold water main
In a larger house, certainly with more than one bathroom, it is preferable to have stored hot water in order to provide adequate volume. This can be achieved by using a cold water mains fed 'Unvented Cylinder' instead of a combination boiler.

will find condensing boilers. These boilers recover heat that ordinary boilers lose through the flue. They are about 1½ times the price of ordinary boilers and, because early models were problematic, some more conservative installers are still reluctant to install them. Condensing boilers may sometimes produce a 'plume' of mist (from the flue discharge) particularly on cold damp mornings. If yours will be pointing towards your neighbour's side passage it could prove embarrassing. Non-condensing boilers should have a seasonal efficiency in the range of 78-85 per cent. Ask any contractor who is providing you with a quotation for heating which boiler he intends to use. As a guide: changing from an old boiler c.1970-80 to a modern non-condensing boiler could result in a 13 per cent fuel saving for a typical semi-detached house. Changing to a condensing boiler in the same situation could result in a saving of 26 per cent.

Combination boilers, which provide both heating and instantaneous hot water for the hot taps, are much loved of contractors because they are simpler to install. They are mostly unsuitable for larger houses (where there is a greater distance between boiler and hot water outlets) and for any house with two bathrooms, because there will only be enough hot water volume to serve one outlet at a time. In smaller houses and flats, combination boilers are excellent and will produce an endless supply of hot water very efficiently.

Discuss the routing of pipework and how much will be seen. If you have timber floors, the pipework should be installed within the floor space (pipework below ground floors should be insulated). If you have solid floors the pipework can be boxed in or installed in purpose made floor ducts (copper pipes must not be buried in the floor screed). Visible pipework in living areas, except between floor and radiator, is unnecessary in most cases. Poorly supported pipework can cause noise and can be damaged. 15mm pipe should be supported at least every 1.4 metres and at each change of direction. Larger sizes can have supports a little further apart.

New copper heating and water piping may need to have 'supplementary bonding' to the electrical system (this is to prevent electric shock in the event of a current carrying conductor coming into contact with this metalwork). If your plumber is unaware of the rules contact an electrician.

Figs. 17a and 17b show typical arrangements for heating and hot and cold water services.

ELECTRICAL WORK

– All electrical work is to be undertaken by a qualified electrician (who is NICEIC or ECA registered*) and carried out in accordance with the latest edition of the IEE** regulations. An appropriate test certificate is to be issued on completion of any work.

* *Trade associations – see Appendix 7 for contact details.*
** The Institute of Electrical Engineers. *The IEE Regulations form the bible for standards in the electrical contracting industry.*

Fortunately, whilst many builders will do their own heating and plumbing work, few will 'have a go' at electrical work. Bad plumbing can cause a lot of damage but bad electrical work can kill. Always insist that your contractor is, or uses, a qualified electrician.

You may wish to specify locations of electrical outlets or discuss them with the contractor and then confirm what has been agreed. Make sure you allow for enough – it is easier to add one before the work starts than later. Generally, 2-3 in each bedroom (think about bedside lights), 3-5 in a living room, 4-6 in a kitchen, 1-2 in a hallway and NONE IN A BATHROOM (only shaver sockets allowed).

Fig. 18 shows a typical layout of electrical circuits.

NOTCHING AND DRILLING JOISTS FOR INSTALLATION OF PIPEWORK AND CABLING

Fig. 19 shows the permitted sizes and locations for these services in order to comply with the Building Regulations.

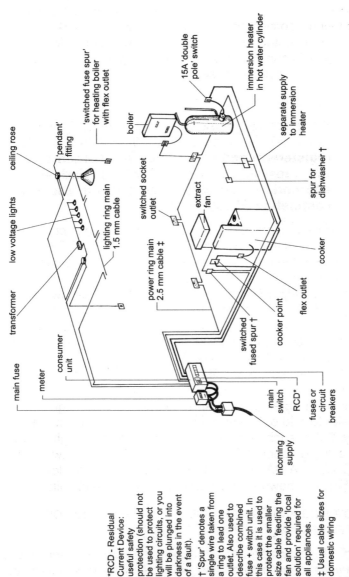

*RCD - Residual Current Device: useful safety protection (should not be used to protect lighting circuits, or you will be plunged into darkness in the event of a fault).

† 'Spur' denotes a single wire taken from a ring to lead one outlet. Also used to describe combined fuse + switch unit. In this case it is used to protect the smaller size cable feeding the fan and provide 'local solution' required for all appliances.

‡ Usual cable sizes for domestic wiring

Fig 18 Electrical circuits

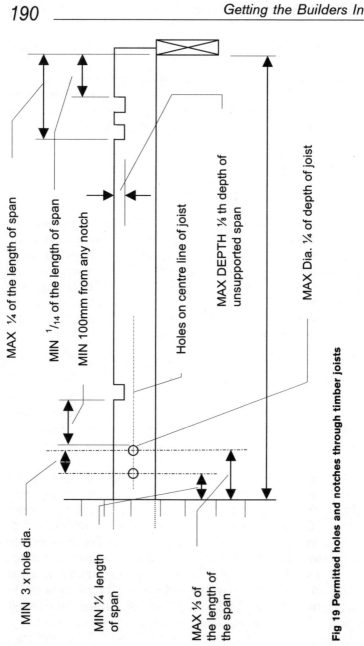

Fig 19 Permitted holes and notches through timber joists

Generally, pipework is installed in notches and cables through holes.

The critical points, structurally, in any beam or joist are the centre and the very ends. For this reason pipework and cabling running across joists should be run around the perimeter of the room a little way from the walls.

OTHER ITEMS

SANITARYWARE, FITTED FURNITURE, ETC.

Always make your own selections. With sanitaryware, it's worth looking in high class showrooms, taking notes and then seeing what price can be obtained for the same items from local merchants. List required items in your brief and ask the contractor to indicate the cost separately. The contractor's price should be close to the price you would pay yourself: his extra discount will be his 'margin' and your insurance if there are any problems.

CONSERVATORIES

It is unlikely that you will have the option of providing much of a brief for a conservatory because in most cases nowadays these are manufactured from 'standard' materials and predetermined patterns. There are, however, a number of points to look out for.

Firstly, the cost of heating a conservatory throughout the winter to the same level as a sitting room is generally prohibitive and contrary to requirements for energy conservation. Conservatories should therefore be connected to the main house via draught proof doors. For a moderate increase in heating bills, however, the installation of central heating will enable use in milder spring or autumn weather and can provide a lower but above freezing temperature to suit tender plants. Not all builders of conservatories will have sufficient knowledge of central heating to be able to advise you fully on this so you may want to speak to a specialist. Underfloor heating using special polyethylene pipework (NOT copper pipework laid in the screed – which has been known!) is popular with conservatories and does not take up limited wall space. Whatever the heating system, it should be capable of being separately controlled from the rest of the house so that it can be turned off completely or set to a lower temperature. (Consider frost protection of the heating pipework.) Separate electric heating is an option but this will be more expensive to run than radiators linked to a gas central heating system.

The construction of conservatories is sometimes carried out by firms as an extension to their double glazing business because the two businesses have a commonality of materials. This means that the traditional elements of the construction are often subcontracted to a general builder or carried out by employees with rudimentary building knowledge. The result can be a lack of sound building experience at higher levels within the firm. This, combined with the fact that there may be no necessity for Building Control inspection, can leave the client alone in monitoring construction standards.

Most conservatories, being lightweight in comparison to other structures, are constructed on a simple concrete slab with no real foundation. In some cases this is adequate but on some soils (clay particularly), a more robust construction should be used. It is worth asking each prospective contractor what kind of base they will sit the conservatory on and what precautions they will take to minimise any movement. A comprehensive answer should indicate at least some understanding of the question! As usual, "Oh don't worry about that" is not a comprehensive answer. Some companies will insist that you engage a builder to lay the base. The advice of a structural engineer would be a worthwhile investment.

Another result of the lightweight nature of conservatories is that in extreme weather there is a possibility that wind can enter through any door to outside and lift the thing off the ground – rather as an umbrella is pulled from your hands on a windy day. Permanent ventilation at roof level will avoid this. Both ventilation and shading should be considered to minimise heat build up in the summer.

Finally, with large conservatories, it is important that the structural members can cope with the wind loading imposed on large surfaces. Extra strong vertical members or cross bracing may be required to give extra support. If you can lean heavily against anything and it gives – it is not strong enough.

SCAFFOLDING

– **Scaffolding shall be erected and maintained in accordance with BS 5973 and 5974 'Access and working scaffolds and special scaffold structures in steel' and The Construction (Health Safety and Welfare) Regulations 1996.**

 No ropes, ladders, pulley blocks or other projections shall be left trailing from the scaffolding outside working hours. No materials shall be left on the scaffolding overnight. All standards, bracing poles, etc., in the vicinity of entrances shall be taped, painted or otherwise treated to improve visibility. Scaffolding above entrances shall be fully boarded at all times with adequate fan* or other protection to prevent people from being struck by falling objects.

 * A close boarded canopy extending out from the scaffolding to protect a public area below from falling objects.

A high proportion of building industry accidents arise from poor erection or use of 'temporary work platforms'. This area remains the responsibility of the contractor (provided that it is part of his contract) but collapse or even falling materials can result in damage and serious or fatal injury, so you should police this area of work carefully. Because of the potential dangers, scaffolding is the subject of much Health and Safety regulation and it is worth quoting appropriate standards where scaffolding is used. This may increase the price from contractors who would otherwise use a cowboy scaffolding firm but the risk may not only be theirs. Fig. 20 demonstrates the points to watch.

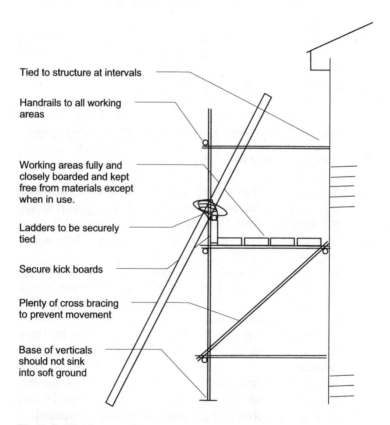

Tied to structure at intervals

Handrails to all working areas

Working areas fully and closely boarded and kept free from materials except when in use.

Ladders to be securely tied

Secure kick boards

Plenty of cross bracing to prevent movement

Base of verticals should not sink into soft ground

Fig 20 Scaffolding – points to watch

Appendix 4:

Planning Regulations

The full Planning requirements are extensive and different rules and emphases may apply in different local authority areas. The following gives general guidance only. If in doubt, consult your local Planning Authority.

EXTENSIONS, LOFT CONVERSIONS, CONSERVATORIES, ETC.

Permission required if:

a)   Any part of the extension is nearer to the highway than the existing property (unless even the extension would still be 20 metres from the highway).

b)   The extension is higher than the highest part of the original structure.*

c)   Any part of the extension is more than 4 metres high and is within 2 metres of the boundary to the property.

d)   The property is a terraced house (including end of terrace) or is in a conservation area** and the volume of the original property* would be increased by more than 10 per cent or 50 cubic metres (whichever is the greater).

e)   Above does not apply but the volume of the original property* would be increased by more than 15 per cent or 70 cubic metres (whichever is the greater).

f)   You live in a conservation area** and you wish to build any extension or any addition which would materially alter the shape of the roof.

195

g)   You intend to build an addition to any roof slope which faces the highway.

h)   The roof extension would add more than 40 cubic metres to the volume of a terraced house or more than 50 cubic metres to any other kind of house.

NEW BUILDINGS OR STRUCTURES (E.G. NEW OUTBUILDINGS, GARAGES, ETC.)

Permission required if:

a)   The new structure would be nearer to the highway than the original structure* as a) above.

b)   As b) above.

c)   The building or structure is not to be used for domestic purposes.

d)   The structure will be more than 3 metres high or more than 4 metres high if it has a ridged roof.

e)   If the existing building is listed or in a conservation area**.

PORCHES

Permission required if:

a)   The porch would have a ground area of more than 3 square metres (measured externally).

b)   It would be higher than 3 metres above ground level.

c)   It would be less than 2 metres away from the boundary with a highway.

FENCES, WALL AND GATES

Permission required if:

a)   The building is listed or within the curtilage of a listed building.

b)   It would be over 1 metre high and next to a highway or over 2 metres high elsewhere.

No permission is required for planting a hedge or a line of trees unless there is a specific restriction on this in your area.

Planning permission is not required for repairs, maintenance, internal alterations, new roofs, aerial installations, addition of roof lights or solar panels flush (or nearly flush) with the existing roof. Installation of satellite dishes and external cladding will require permission if the property is in a conservation area**.

Special notes on volume limits.

- The volumes mentioned above are as measured externally.
- If the proposed extension is within 5 metres of another building belonging to the property, the volume of that building counts against the allowance, e.g. a detached garage may need to be taken into account when calculating volumes.
- Any existing building over 10 cubic metres in volume and within 5 metres of the original structure, that has been added to the property, will count as an extension and will reduce the allowance for further extension.

* as first built or as it stood on 1st July 1948 if built earlier.

** Conservation areas include, for the purposes of these guidelines, National Parks and areas designated as being "of outstanding natural beauty".

Appendix 5:

Glossary of Construction Terms

Note that Fig. 21 illustrates many construction terms.

AAV: Air admittance valve or 'automatic air vent'. A device to allow air to escape from high points in a heating system.

Architrave: Moulded frame around doors and openings to cover the joint between the wall and the timber casing of the opening.

Balanced flue (on a gas appliance): A duct that allows both fresh (combustion air) in and products of combustion out.

Ballast: Sand and 'aggregate' (stones) for mixing with cement (and water) to form concrete.

Ballast [2]: Control gear for fluorescent lighting.

Benching: Sloping concrete at the base of a manhole.

Blinding: A covering, usually sand, over hardcore to prevent sharp stones penetrating a damp proof membrane.

Block work: Wall built using precast concrete blocks typically 450mm long x 225mm high x 100mm or 150mm thick. Generally used as the inner skin of a cavity wall and for solid internal walls. Cheaper (per square metre) and usually with better thermal performance than brickwork.

Bonding: The overlapping (interlocking) of successive courses of bricks or blocks producing a regular pattern without vertical joints from one course to the next (the purpose being to strengthen the construction).

Breather membrane: A sheet that allows air and vapour to penetrate but is water resistant. Used under weather resistant coverings to walls or roofs.

BS: British Standard. A document published by the British Standards Institute as a guide to specification and good practice. The whole range covers just about every industry but many cover construction installation, products and materials.

Cavity batten: A strip of timber drawn up between the leaves of a cavity wall to remove excess mortar that may otherwise cause a bridge for moisture and heat-loss.

Cavity closer (tray): A device that sits across the cavity in a cavity wall to prevent moisture from running down the cavity and onto finishes, timber frames or structural members. Moisture is directed to weep holes in the external skin.

Combi-boiler: Combination boiler providing both heating and instantaneous domestic hot water.

Concrete: Mixture of sand, cement and 'coarse aggregate' (stones up to about 20mm).

Condensation: Water droplets that form on a cold surface, the temperature of which is at or below the point (dew point) where water vapour can no longer be held in suspension.

Consumer unit: Main electrical intake box with fuses or circuit breakers and a main switch.

Dabs: Blobs of mortar or adhesive used, for example, to fix lining boards to masonry.

Dpc: Damp proof course; in a wall. Usually mineral felt, thick polythene or other impervious material.

Dpm: Damp proof membrane. As dpc but in sheet form for preventing damp penetration through flat surfaces.

Dry lining: The use of plasterboard or proprietary sheeting on battens or studwork without a surface coat of site applied plaster.

Eaves: The point where the roof meets the wall. Term applied to the arrangement of joining these two surfaces. It includes the timber construction at the top of the wall and the 'fascia', 'soffit' and guttering arrangement.

Elasomeric sheeting: A roof covering that expands and contracts under the sun without cracking or distorting.

Expansion vessel: A small tank that allows water from a heating system to enter and leave as the water expands on heating and contracts on cooling.

Fascia: General term to refer to the face of something but specifically 'fascia board', the vertical board at eaves level that the guttering is fixed to.

Feed and expansion cistern: On a heating system. Does same job as expansion vessel (above) but is open to atmosphere and also allows water to 'top up' the system.

Flashing: A strip of material, traditionally lead or zinc, used to weatherproof a joint between a roof and a wall or a penetration through a roof.

Flaunching: Sloping mortar, usually surrounding a chimney pot, to direct rainwater from brickwork.

Footings: Word commonly used to refer to foundations – although incorrectly. Originally, footings were brick courses placed on the concrete foundation which started wider than the wall thickness and stepped back over 3 or 4 courses to the width of the wall.

Going: The tread on a staircase.

Hardcore:	Generally broken brick and rubble which is consolidated and used as a base for a concrete slab or to cover the soil in suspended floor construction.
Header:	End of a brick.
Hip:	Outside sloping joint where two angles of a pitched roof meet.
Indirect hot water cylinder:	Vessel – usually made of copper – that allows water for the hot taps to be heated by water from the heating system. The heating water passes through a 'coil' in the cylinder so does not mix with the water that goes to the taps.
Interstitial condensation:	Condensation that forms within an external building fabric.
Intumescent mastic:	A filler that expands when in contact with heat so preventing the spread of smoke and retarding the spread of fire.
Joist:	Horizontal structural element, usually timber, to support floors, roofs or to form a ceiling.
Lintel:	Strip of timber, concrete, steel or preformed composite structure, to support the load above an opening and transfer it to the walls on either side.
Low-e glass:	Low emissivity glass. Coated glass with improved thermal performance. Almost essential to meet new Building Regulations for glazing.
LV:	Low voltage. Usually applied to lights or bathroom fans than run, via a transformer, on 12 or 24 volts.
MCCB:	Moulded case circuit breaker. Modern replacement for a fuseholder in a 'consumer unit' which breaks the circuit on detection of overload but can be manually reset.
MDF:	Medium density fibreboard. A dense board resistant to warping and capable of being intricately shaped – used in joinery and furniture making.

Microporous: Waterproof yet allowing moisture vapour to be released (breathable).

Mortar: Mix of sand, cement and sometimes additives to bond brickwork or coat internal brickwork before the application of finishing plaster.

Mullion: Vertical dividing section to windows.

Padstone: Dense material used to transfer the load of a beam to surrounding masonry.

Parapet: Top of a wall where it rises above roof level.

Party wall: A wall that divides two adjoining properties.

Pendant light fitting: One that hangs from the ceiling.

Plasterboard: Sheets (usually 2.4m x 1.2m) of gypsum plaster with a thick paper covering.

Purlin: Horizontal roof member that supports the rafters.

Raft foundation: A style of construction whereby a reinforced concrete floor slab is integrated with a reinforced shallow foundation strip and 'floats' on the subsoil.

Rafter: Sloping timber members that carry the covering of a pitched roof.

Render: Sand and cement mortar used to cover masonry.

Reveal: Sides of a door or window opening.

Ridge: The apex of a pitched roof. The 'ridge board' being the horizontal timber member that runs the length of the roof to which the rafters are connected at either side.

Ring main: Electrical arrangement that joins all outlets in a ring to reduce cable lengths by taking advantage of 'diversity' of load.

Riser: The vertical pieces between the treads on a staircase.

Rising main: Cold water main – so called because it usually rises to the roof space to feed cold water tanks.

RSJ: Rolled steel joist. Used to refer to any steel beam, although inaccurately in most cases.

Screed: A sand and cement mortar, usually finished with a steel trowel to give a smooth floor finish.

Skim: A thin coat of finishing plaster (usually about 3mm) over plasterboard.

Snagging: Items of work requiring remedial work or completion prior to final acceptance of the work as being complete.

Soaker: Sheet material to weather a penetration through a roof.

Soffit: General term indicating the underside of something but particularly 'soffit board', the horizontal boarding at the 'eaves' which runs from the 'fascia' back to the wall.

Soldier course: In brickwork, a row of bricks standing vertically.

Stretcher: The long side of a brick.

String: Sloping edge of a staircase.

Studding (studwork):   Support framework for lightweight wall construction usually timber or metal.

SVP: Soil vent pipe. Same as 'waste stack'. Vertical pipe that takes waste water (etc.) from plumbing apparatus to the drain.

Transome: Horizontal dividing section to windows.

TRV: Thermostatic radiator valve.

'U' value: Thermal transmittance in watts/m^2 °K. A measure of the amount of heat that is lost through an element of building fabric.

UB: Universal beam. 'I' shaped beam often called (erroneously) an RSJ.

UPVC: Unplasticised Polyvinyl Chloride – a synthetic compound (plastic).

Wall tie: A metal connector for tying two skins of a cavity wall.

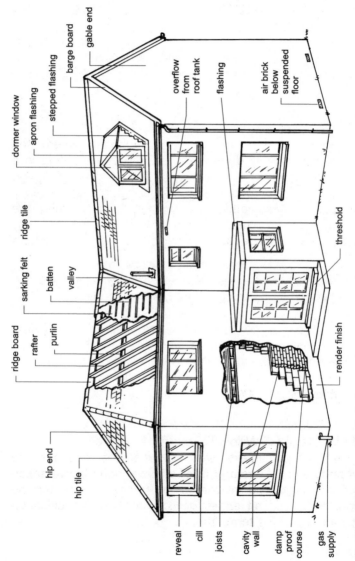

Fig 21 Building terms illustrated

Appendix 6:

Sample Letters

Those whose day-to-day work involves the writing of letters, of complaint or otherwise, will be quite comfortable with composing their own correspondence where appropriate. There are other occupations where the requirement simply does not arise and letter writing is a less familiar task. I include the following as a guide because it is far better to fly off a timely letter, even if adapted from something pre-printed, than to delay the action because composing just the right comments may take some time. Be sure to keep a copy of any letters sent.

SAMPLE LETTER 1 – INVITATION TO TENDER

[Date]

Mr A Jones
Acme Builders Ltd
Construction Row
Ablethorpe AE1 2XY

Dear Mr Jones
Re: Works at 22 Willow Drive
I wish to have an extension constructed to the rear of the property and understand from our telephone conversation that you would be interested in offering a price for the work. I enclose an architect's drawing and specification and a copy of the terms that I wish to use.

I am looking to have the work started after my return from holiday at the end of June. Please contact me to arrange an appointment to call.

Yours sincerely

_____

SAMPLE LETTER 2 – QUERYING TERMS

Dear Mr Jones
Re: Works at 22 Willow Drive
    Thank you for your quotation. I have yet to make final decisions but there is one point that I want to clarify. The terms and conditions that you sent with your proposal exclude a number of things that I consider important. I am happy to accept your clauses 1-5 but I cannot agree your clause 6 requiring final payment linked to time rather than performance. May I suggest that should I choose to award you the contract, we use my terms modified to include your terms 1-5.
    I look forward to hearing from you.

Yours sincerely

_____

SAMPLE LETTER 3 – LETTER OF ACCEPTANCE

Dear Mr Jones
Re: 22 Willow Drive – Extension
    I am pleased to advise you of the acceptance of your quotation for the above work in the sum of £45,720.00. The following documentation shall form the basis of the contract:
    This letter of acceptance.
    My specification and general conditions dated 4th April 20.. (modified as agreed).
    Architect's drawing No. Wil/1.

Structural engineer's sketches 2390/1 and /2.

My sketch showing radiator positions and electrical sockets Sk1.

Your tender dated 13th May 20 . .

My letter dated 23rd May 20 . ., concerning the glazing options.

You have indicated a contract period of six weeks. In order to afford you a little flexibility I am prepared to formalise a contract period of seven weeks. Please advise me of a start date within the next two weeks and the completion date shall hence be seven weeks after this. In accordance with my conditions, you are to provide a detailed programme of works within two weeks.

Payment shall be made in two stages: an interim payment based on work carried out after four weeks and a final payment upon completion and submission of final account.

As discussed on the telephone, I would like us to meet again before you start work, either on the day you start or before. Please telephone me to advise start date and to arrange this meeting.

Yours sincerely

SAMPLE LETTER 4A

RECORDING DISSATISFACTION WITH THE CONTRACTOR – HEATING

Dear Mr Jones

Re: 22 Willow Drive – rear extension

Last Tuesday the 8th September I pointed out to your foreman Jim, that the central heating needs to be brought back into working order because I shall soon need to turn it on.

I am not prepared to use electric heating when I have a perfectly good heating system, simply because there is an open end where you have yet to connect a radiator.

I trust that the matter will be resolved this week.

SAMPLE LETTER 4B

RECORDING DISSATISFACTION WITH THE CONTRACTOR – ROOFING

Dear Mr Jones
Re: 22 Willow Drive – rear extension
I have advised your roofing contractor that I am not happy with the flashing between the extension roof and the side wall. It looks to me that, if there is a severe downpour, I will have a flood in my sitting room. After two weeks this matter has not been attended to.

Please ensure that the matter is dealt with before the coming weekend.

SAMPLE LETTER 4C – ADVISING OF POTENTIAL 'CONTRA' CHARGES

Dear Mr Jones
Re: 22 Willow Drive – rear extension
There has been no improvement in progress since my previous letter. You will recall that the completion date of this contract was fixed at 31st July because this is the date when I must move out of my old home. If the property is not ready for my occupation on 1st August I will need to arrange hotel accommodation. I shall consider this an unnecessary expense occasioned by your failure to comply with the contract and shall be looking to your firm to meet any costs incurred.

Yours sincerely
See Chapter 12, page 132, as to whether or not you have a right under the contract to deduct expenses from the contractor's account.

SAMPLE LETTER 5A GIVE AN ULTIMATUM – HEATING

Dear Mr Jones
Re: 22 Willow Drive – rear extension
    I have had no response to my previous letter about the heating. Unless the matter is resolved before next Wednesday 16th September I will be forced to employ a heating engineer to make good the installation so that it can be put into operation. The costs involved in this action will be deducted from your account.

SAMPLE LETTER 5B GIVE AN ULTIMATUM – FAILURE TO PERFORM

Dear Mr Jones
Re: 22 Willow Drive – rear extension
    Despite my letter of [date] there has been no labour on site since [date] and, according to your programme, the work is now two weeks behind. I must insist that the progress is restored by the end of this week or I shall be forced to consider taking further action.

SAMPLE LETTER 6 FINAL DEMAND

RECORDED DELIVERY

Dear Mr Jones
Re: 22 Willow Drive – rear extension
    Having had no adequate response to my two previous letters of [dates] I am afraid you leave me with no alternative but to [client to choose from below]:
    Either:
    [contact the [e.g. Federation of Master Builders] with a view to getting a third party to inspect the works.]
    or:

[consider terminating the contract unless work is resumed within the next three days.]

SAMPLE LETTER 7 TO M D OF COMPANY

Mr T Mann
Clear Proof Double Glazing Ltd
14 Canalside
Worthripple-on-Sea WE1 2ZZ

RECORDED DELIVERY

Dear Mr Mann
Re: Works to the above address, your contract No. CPDG/ 2003

I wish to draw your attention to a contract for a double-glazing installation with which your company has every reason to be extremely embarrassed.

The work commenced four weeks after the original agreed date due to material difficulties. Because of this, I expected your firm to make a particular effort to have the work carried out within reasonable time. On the contrary, the rear of my house has been a building site now for nearly four weeks. I wrote to your contracts manager Mrs Middle seven days ago but have received no reply. Frankly, Mr Mann, my experience with your company suggests that you have little regard for your customers once they have paid their deposit. I trust, now that you are aware of the problem and would not wish your company's performance on this contract to become any more public, you will ensure that progress is restored within three days and the work completed by the end of next Friday (18th April).

I am sure you will be able to sort this matter out to avoid our mutual relationship deteriorating further but if you cannot arrange for substantial progress to be made within 4-5 days I shall have no alternative but to consider your firm in breach of contract (by virtue of the implied terms afforded by the Sale of Goods and Services Act 1972). In the event that I elect to terminate the contract, I shall be looking to your firm to meet any costs.

SAMPLE LETTER 8 – TERMINATION

RECORDED DELIVERY

Dear Mr Jones
Re: 22 Willow Drive – rear extension

There has been no labour on site for three weeks and you have failed to respond adequately to my previous correspondence. I advised you on 3rd July that I considered you to be in breach of contract and you have made no attempt to remedy this breach. I am therefore terminating this contract forthwith.

You have left a number of pieces of equipment here which you may collect by appointment. I shall be preparing a final account and will send this to you in due course.

SAMPLE LETTER 9 – TERMINATION – TAKING OVER OF SUBCONTRACTORS

RECORDED DELIVERY

Dear Mr Jones
Re: 22 Willow Drive – rear extension

You have made no attempt to remedy the breach of contract occasioned by your failure to perform for 3 weeks.

It is my intention to terminate the contract with your firm. I shall be employing a surveyor who will discuss the final account with you, and his costs will be deducted from your account as damages.

It is my intention to enter into direct contracts with Messrs Plumb Spark to complete the subcontract works.

Please contact me to arrange an appointment to collect your equipment.

_____

SAMPLE LETTER 10 – REMEDIAL WORK UNDER GUARANTEE

Dear Mr Jones
Re: 22 Willow Drive – rear extension
    I have asked you on three occasions to attend to the flaking of the mortar between the rear steps and the side wall. I must insist that this remedial work is put in hand within the next two weeks or I shall have to engage another contractor to do the repair and look to you for reimbursement of the costs.

Yours sincerely

Appendix 7:

Useful Names and Addresses

Association of Plumbing and Heating Contractors (APHC)	Tel: 0800 542 6060
British Decorators Association	32 Coton Road, Nuneaton Warwickshire CV11 5TW Tel: 024 7635 3776
Chartered Institute of Arbitrators	24 Angel Gate, City Road London EC1V 2RS Tel: 020 7421 7444
Chartered Institute of Building Services Engineers (CIBSE)	222 Balham High Road London SW12 9BS Tel: 020 8675 5211 Website: www.cibse.org
Confederation of Roofing Contractors	72 Church Road Brightlingsea Colchester, Essex CO7 0JF Tel: 01206 306600
Construction Industry Training Board	Tel: 01485 577577
CORGI (The Council for Registered Gas Installers)	1 Elmwood Chineham Business Park Crockford Lane Basingstoke Hants RG24 8WG Tel: 01256 372200

Electrical Contractors' Association (ECA)	ESCA House 34 Palace Court London W2 4HY Tel: 020 7313 4800
Fair Trades	Tel: 08707 38 48 58
Federation of Master Builders (FMB)	Gordon Fisher House 14-15 Great James Street London WC1N 3DP Tel: 020 7242 7583 Fax: 020 7404 0296 E-mail: central@fmb.org.uk
Glass and Glazing Federation (GGF)	Glass and Glazing Federation 44-48 Borough High Street London SE1 1XB Tel: 020 7403 7177 Fax: 020 7357 7458 E-mail: info@ggf.org.uk
Guild of Master Craftsmen	Castle Place 166 High Street Lewes East Sussex BN7 1XU Tel: 01273 478449
Heating and Ventilating Contractors' Association (HVCA)	ESCA House 34 Palace Court London W2 4HY Tel: 020 7313 4900
Homepro	Tel: 08707 344 344
Institute of Domestic Heating and Environmental Engineers (IDHEE)	Dorchester House Wimblestraw Road Berinsfield Wallingford Oxford OX10 7LZ Tel: 01865 343096

Institute of Plumbing (IOP)	64 Station Lane Hornchurch Essex RM12 6NB Tel: 01708 472791
Institute of Quality Assurance (IQA)	Tel: 020 7245 6722
Institution of Structural Engineers (I Struct.E)	11 Upper Belgrave Street London SW1X 8BH Tel: 020 7235 4535 Website: www.istructe.org.uk
League of Professional Craftsmen	Suite 111 Marlborough House 159 High Street Wealdstone Middlesex HA3 5DX Tel: 020 8427 8934
National Federation of Roofing Contractors	Tel: 020 7436 0387
National Inspection Council for Electrical Installation Contracting (NICEIC)	Vintage House 37 Albert Embankment London SE1 7UJ Tel: 020 7564 2323 Fax: 020 7564 2370 E-mail: enquiries@niceic.org.uk Technical Helpline: 020 7564 2320
Quality Mark Scheme	Tel: 0845 300 80 40
Royal Institute of British Architects (RIBA)	66 Portland Place London W1B 1AD Tel: 020 7307 3700 Website: www.architecture.com

Website:
www.ribabookshops.com

Royal Institute of Chartered
Surveyors (RICS)

12 Great George Street
Parliament Square
London SW1P 3AD
Tel: 020 7222 7000

RESOURCES

Trading Standards Office

For advice if you have a
dispute or are unhappy
with your contractor

Contact your local authority
– Town Hall

County Court

For information about
taking a contractor to
court

Find in local telephone
directory

The Building Centre

For those within reach of
(or who fancy a trip to)
London, this is an excellent
resource centre with a
permanent exhibition of
building products and
materials, a building
bookshop and a vast range
of product literature.

26 Store Street, London
WC1E 7BT
Tel: 020 7692 4000
Website:
www.buildingcentre.co.uk

Public Libraries

Most central libraries have a 'building construction' section. The *Barbour Index* and similar compendiums show a
range of building products.

Builders merchants

A visit to a good merchants, when it is quiet, may find very knowledgeable staff who will be happy to offer advice.

Location of services underground

Gas:	**– Contact regional office of Transco in UK**
Electricity:	**– Contact regional network maintenance contractor (your electricity supplier should be able to give you details)**
Water:	**– Contact your regional Water Authority**

Planning and Building Control Departments of local authorities may have websites providing information about applying for permission and even application forms that you can download.

Building Regulations

Copies of the 'Approved Documents' can be obtained from libraries or can be downloaded free from the *Office of the Deputy Prime Minister* website (www.odpm.gov.uk).

Appendix 8:

Example Statement and Claim for 'Damages'

The following is based on proceedings in a Small Claims Court. If you intend to issue proceedings in a County Court you should take legal advice and work with that adviser in drawing up the appropriate documents.

THE STATEMENT BELOW IS BASED ON A DISPUTE WITH THE FOLLOWING SCENARIO:

The contractor completed a proportion of work then vanished from site.

- Some of the work carried out was of poor quality and remedial works were required.
- Despite several requests, the contractor failed to put right the faulty work.
- A second contractor was engaged to rectify faulty work and complete the job.

Competitive prices should be obtained for the usual reasons but also to demonstrate that the amount of your claim is 'reasonable'.

The claim is made for 'costs' against the first contractor for the cost of the remedial works. Only the cost of the remedial works can be claimed. If the second contractor's price for completing the works is greater than the first contractor's price, that's too bad! It does not constitute a 'loss', so cannot be claimed against the defaulting contractor (it may be the fact that the first contractor's price was too low that has led him to cut corners and abandon the job!).

You should set out as clearly as possible the facts of your claim and the sequence of events. You should also show that you have made an effort to resolve your dispute with the contractor.

The court forms should be completed with your details (you are the 'claimant' – may be called the Plaintiff on some forms), and the details of the contractor against whom you are making the claim (the 'Respondent' – may be called the Defendant on some forms). You may write your statement of claim in the space on the form or, preferably, write "attached" on the form, next to 'Statement (or Particulars) of Claim' and append a typed sheet with: "STATEMENT OF CLAIM" at the top.

The following indicates typical wording and the detail that you should include.

STATEMENT OF CLAIM

1. A contract for certain building works was entered into on 1st June 2002 between the claimant and the respondent. The contract was instigated by written acceptance (on 1st June) of the respondent's quotation dated 2nd May 2002 based on the claimant's brief dated 5th April 2002. (attached)[1]
2. It was agreed between the claimant and the respondent that the work should take four weeks and this was confirmed in writing by the claimant's letter to the respondent dated 6th June 2002.
3. The work commenced on 10th June 2002. After three weeks and partial completion of the work the respondent failed to return to site. Several telephone calls and three letters (appended) were sent to request the respondent's return to complete the work, the last of which (dated 15th July) being notification that another contractor would be engaged to complete the work.

4.   Three quotations were obtained for a replacement contractor and the lowest was Messrs. Tidy & Finnish Ltd., for the sum of £6,300 inclusive of VAT.

5.   All three quotations (copies attached) highlighted the respondent's faulty work. The respondent was contacted once more (my letter dated 6th August 2002) to advise him of the faulty work and to give him the opportunity to rectify it. No reply was received.

6.   Messrs. Tidy & Finnish (the replacement contractor) were engaged to rectify the faulty work and complete the job.

7.   The amount of the works that Messrs. Tidy & Finnish carried out to rectify faulty work amounts to £2,200 plus VAT. A full list of defects and costs is appended.

8.   A copy of the claimant's brief is attached and details of required workmanship standards are highlighted. Also attached is a copy of a letter from Messrs. Tidy & Finnish confirming that the work carried out by the respondent did not meet the standards set out in the brief.[2]

AMOUNT OF CLAIM

The claimant claims the sum of £2,200 (together with VAT paid) and damages of £250[3] or such sums as the court may consider appropriate for the inconvenience arising from the respondent's breach of contract.

NOTES

[1]   It is more professional to number the appended documents and submit them in a bundle with the court form. The numbers should then be referred to in the text.

[2]   In a complex dispute, such a letter from an independent surveyor would carry more weight.

[3]   Damages, if awarded, will be at the discretion of the court.

Index